LITTLE WIDE-AWAKE

An Anthology

FROM

VICTORIAN CHILDREN'S BOOKS

AND PERIODICALS

IN THE COLLECTION OF

ANNE AND FERNAND G. RENIER

SELECTED BY

LEONARD DE VRIES

THE WORLD PUBLISHING COMPANY

CLEVELAND AND NEW YORK

ACKNOWLEDGEMENTS

Leonard de Vries is very much indebted to Mr. F.G. and Mrs Anne Renier for all their help and for allowing him to make use of their extensive library.

Acknowledgements are also due to Constable Publishers Ltd for permission to quote from *Songs for Little People* by Norman Gale and to Gerald Duckworth & Co. Ltd for permission to include *The New Mother* by Mrs. W. K. Clifford.

CONTENTS

INTRODUCTION
by M. F. Thwaite

Victorian children's books are as remarkable for their striking contrasts, changing patterns of thought and fashion, and progress towards emancipation and enrichment as was the era they served. No anthology could reflect all their facets—their vitality, shoddiness, charm, crudity, sentimentality, melodrama, tenderness and soaring imagination. For this was the best of times and the worst of times for the young reader. An age of light bringing in great creative writing and originality, an age of darkness spreading mediocrity and sensationalism. If it touched the stars it also sank to the gutter.

This anthology by Leonard de Vries is a personal selection of texts and pictures from a few of the many thousands of Victorian children's books in the private library of F.G. and Anne Renier—the finest collection of juvenile Victoriana, very likely, outside the national libraries. The compiler is already well-known for his *Flowers of Delight*, a delectable bouquet gathered from children's books of 1765 to 1830 in the Osborne collection at Boys and Girls House, Toronto. An earlier volume, *Bloempjes der Vreugd*, representing old Dutch children's books from 1712 to 1898, was published in Amsterdam, and is little known over here.

The verses, stories, little episodes and pictures he has chosen for this present book are taken almost entirely from the secondary and ephemeral literature of the period. They may be regarded as curious and interesting examples of what was read by children (especially those of tenderer years) during the sixty years following the accession of Victoria, or as a peepshow into a fascinating and almost forgotten way of life.

In the harsher earlier years of the young Queen's reign and the divided society of Disraeli's "Two Nations", the Rich and the Poor, there was a great difference between the reading matter available for their children. For young people working in field or factory, at least for those fortunate enough to read at all, there were supplies of tiny tracts, such as *Bob the Cabin Boy*, the story of Susan and Betsy in *Temper*, and other examples in this anthology. Reading the Bible was always the prime purpose, but these tracts (published by many London and provincial firms, but still headed by the pioneer Religious Tract Society founded in 1799) were intended to present a simpler and more dramatic introduction to religious knowledge. They were supported by an increasing number of Sunday School periodicals, sectarian journals, and missionary magazines, filled with similar pious, proselytising and fervent matter. Some tracts (and surely that amazing tirade of threats, *The Swearer's Prayer*, was one of them) were aimed at the poorer classes in general not only their offspring. And if they presented religion in a sensational form the purpose was to compete with profane competitors in the field. For there were also to be had pennyworths and halfpennyworths of worldly, lurid or entertaining fare—sometimes flimsy copies for a farthing. These were the heirs of the chapbooks. A notable provider was the Catnach Press of Seven Dials,—claiming to be of its kind "the oldest and cheapest House in the World"—but it had numerous rivals, among them J. March, whose penny series is represented by *The Misfortunes of Toby Ticklepitcher* and other titles.

For the well-shod little inmates of comfortable nurseries and schoolrooms there was a much wider choice of reading matter. Many prettily adorned productions were to be had, often "plain or coloured", but certainly costing more than the legendary penny or twopence. John Harris, at the top of Ludgate Hill, had started the vogue for hand-coloured alternatives to uncoloured versions early in the nineteenth century, especially in a new series of fanciful little works which included that popular success, *The Butterfly's Ball*. He was soon to have many imitators, and his successors at the end of the 1830s carried on the traditions he founded. A little later another enterprising publisher and book-designer, Joseph Cundall, brought fresh distinction to books for younger children. He had produced the well-designed "Home Treasury" series for Sir Henry Cole in the forties, and was responsible, both on his own, and with his partner Addey, for other tasteful and pleasing issues, some excellently printed by Charles Whittingham. Two examples of his "Pleasure Books for Young Children", published in association with David Bogue, have been included—*Maja's Alphabet* and *Little Mary's Picture Riddles*. These show how old-fashioned themes—the perennial alphabet and riddle books for children—could be shaped into new and appealing form at the middle of the century.

Though more privileged boys and girls had a much wider choice and more amusement in their books than had those of humbler station, in these earlier decades, the urge to instruct, to improve, to inculcate religious beliefs was still dominant in much of their literature. Two very much approved works offering religious teaching in a well-presented and easy form were *The History of the Fairchild Family*, by Mrs. Sherwood (the first part issued in 1818), and the *Divine Songs* of Isaac Watts, now in its second century, and learnt by heart by all classes of children. But new if lesser rivals had appeared. One of them included here is Mrs. Favel Lee Mortimer's *Peep of Day*, a naive little work designed for the very young. Similar serious intentions, for older readers, preoccupy the author of another example, *The Boy's Week Day Book*, first published the same year, 1833, but like *Peep of Day*, revised and reprinted for Victorian children. He set out to show young people, in the fashion of the 1830s, but in a rather more disarming style than usual, how they might be happy by fearing God and doing their duty. Salvation assured, a boy could then find plenty of innocent amusement, although thought for the future in this life and the next is never far away. Typical as it is, it foreshadows the nature of books to come, for cheerfulness is beginning to invade the moral and religious manual. It points towards the rapid advance of a less dogmatic approach in writing for children. And with the arrival of the first of the Hans Andersen stories and the first nonsense limericks of Edward Lear in 1846, a flush of bright sunrise illumines the scene.

This promise of wonder, fairy-lore and laughter in children's books did not mean that other ideas were not prevalent. There was, for example, the "Peter Parley" school, firmly convinced that the young mind needed neither fairy tales nor religious doctrine, but facts about the everyday world. Its originator was an American, Samuel G. Goodrich, but his books and his *nom-de-plume* were widely imitated here, and in the present volume *Inquisitive Jack* is a characteristic example. This is an English edition of an original "Peter Parley", published by Goodrich in 1846, as *The Truth-finder*.

As the railway age speeded ahead (it may be noticed that even the new iron monster could be used to point a religious lesson in a penny tract), books for youth multiplied as fast as the population. Their themes and subjects began to match the variety of the new territories of Britain's growing Empire. By the time the Queen and Empress celebrated her Diamond Jubilee in 1897 what a transformation had taken place! A new secular literature for all ages of young Britons had come into being, bringing many kinds of knowledge, adventure, wonder and romance within reach of the millions now being taught the three "R"'s in the "Board" schools provided for compulsory if limited education by the State. Long series of cheap editions, made possible through mass production and technical improvements in book-production, and provision for children by public libraries (at least within the towns) were helping to bring good literature within the reach of the poorer child. So that the gap between Rich and Poor, as far as reading matter was concerned, was narrowing.

There was still plenty of serious purpose to be found in children's books, however. But it had now become much softened and sentimentalised. The fairy, dream-centred parable, *Harry's Rash Wish*, is an example. Mrs. W. K. Clifford, wife of the well-known mathematician and philosopher, also wrote many tales embodying the new fanciful and sentimental approach to admonition. From her *Anyhow Stories* Mr. de Vries has selected the one example which shows a capacity to be really terrifying in a subtle and original fashion. The theme of *The New Mother* —children deprived of a loving mother by the substitution of a monster, as a retribution for naughtiness—goes much further in real terror than any theological strictures of Mrs. Sherwood and her kind. Yet the other tales by Mrs. Clifford have nothing of this horror of children being "castaways". Most of them are sentimental, idealistic inventions, often sad, but never frightening.

By the 1890s there was a new patriotic pride to satisfy as well as continuing help to be mustered for the destitute and unfortunate. This more martial and imperial note is heard in verses like *The Band of the Red, White and Blue* —a rousing call to young readers to help the children who still "pine in rags for bread". This appeal for charitable pennies appeared in *The Infant's Magazine* in 1891. By this date all kinds of children's periodicals and annuals, both the cheap and wholesome, such as *Chatterbox* (founded 1866) and the *Boy's Own Paper* (founded 1879), and their rivals purveying incredibility and sensation, had greatly multiplied.

Among the promoters of inexpensive, purposeful and simple journals for youth was the famous Dr. Barnardo. After he had set up his East End Juvenile Mission in 1867, he edited the *Children's Treasury*, available at a halfpenny, Drawing Room edition one penny. From 1881 this became *Our Darlings* in a new and enlarged form. The aim throughout was to gain friends and fellow-workers "on behalf of the dear children under my care, the sorrowful and neglected little 'waifs and strays' of our great cities", as well as to spread Christian teaching.

A submerged England of wretched children had been depicted forcefully and unforgettably by Dickens, and his description of the death of Jo, the poor "moved-on" boy of the streets, "knowin' nothink", was one of his most impassioned appeals to authority. This state of things still existed when Dr. Barnardo came to London from Ireland in the 1860s. None of the extracts from Dr. Barnardo's periodicals which appear in this anthology expresses his great Christian work more vividly than the illustration from No. 76 of the *Children's Treasury*, where a kindly man is welcoming a poor little girl.

Mr. de Vries's selections reveal how much religious indoctrination permeated Victorian books for children, especially in the earlier years, when it was usually of a melodramatic and evangelical nature. Much of this repels the modern reader, but in its day it seems to have been triumphantly effective and much in demand. Long drawn out death scenes (a typical feature of Victorian fiction), such as the fate of the little boy bitten by a mad dog, were apparently a source of horrific or inspiring enjoyment, for what did all the protracted sufferings matter, if the little victim died with the words "Happy! Happy!" on his lips ? A celestial home, a Heaven as beautiful as fairyland, awaited these young souls. Death was not the conqueror but a way to "A Better Land". The dead child with the holly in his hand, fetched by the angels to join his Mamma, is meant to be pathetic but not mournful. No scene is more characteristic of its period, and nothing has changed more in children's books than the attitude to death and religion.

There was a less serious and more practical kind of didactic writing for the young inherited by the Victorians, like much else, from an earlier generation. This was concerned with avoiding the evil consequences of irrational or imprudent conduct, and it has been dubbed the "awful warning" class of literature. It is exemplified in the advice given in *Furze and Heather for Rainy Weather*, a section of *Birdie's Book*, in 1880. New inventions brought fresh hazards as Master Andrew found in playing with gas. This kind of admonition was presented in more pleasing and playful style in the verses of Ann and Jane Taylor, popular favourites ever since their publication in the first decade of the century. The Taylors wrote other simple little rhymes on nature and everyday things, and one poem, "Twinkle, twinkle, little star", is still not forgotten. Some of their verses (shorn of much detail and persuasive advice) appear also in *Birdie's Book*, under the grandiloquent headings— *Little Mites for Tiny Sprites*, and *Titbits for Tiny Wits*.

This survival of earlier and influential children's books for enjoyment by later generations shows that young readers are never restricted to books written for them by contemporary authors, although old favourites are usually reshaped and newly illustrated to suit changing taste. Another popular book, dating from 1786, was Mrs. Trimmer's story about a family of redbreasts, *Fabulous Histories*, intended for her own children. Like many books which followed it, the purpose was to combine the inculcation of moral principles with instruction "respecting the proper treatment of animals". Prized in Victorian nurseries under its later title, *The History of the Robins*, it appears here as a little picture book, *A Welcome Guest from Robin's Nest*. The formidable chapters of the original have been reduced to a few simple sentences to explain each picture. Books pleading for kindness to animals go back to the publications of John Newbery, and they were sometimes amplified with horrific, even suggestive examples of cruelty, like those detailed in the second chapter of the *Boy's Week Day Book*. But later in the nineteenth century animals and pets steadily become sentimentalised, and harsh realism is excluded, as in the tender little tale of *The Toy Duck*. After the classic tale, *Black Beauty*, had begun to charm generations of little readers in 1877, stories and pictures about animals become as plentiful in children's books as apples in autumn.

The gush of sentiment which began to flow into Victorian books for youth from about the middle of the century stemmed from a changing attitude to the child. Childhood was becoming enveloped in a rose-mist of idealism, and the child was soon to be the centre of his own mysterious and magical world. "A new unpietistic handling of childhood" was supplanting earlier oppressive treatment, and children were somehow becoming naturally good, younger and more innocent. Childhood was being less looked upon as a training ground for the future, and more as an idyllic period to be cherished and prolonged. Even Mrs. Sherwood's grimmer episodes were expurgated from *The Fairchild Family*, for to her (and others of her persuasion) the child was naturally evil, steeped in original sin, which must be eradicated by fearsome example and punishment.

The emancipated and more indulged children of these later decades are personified by the stylish little lady on the cover, a picture taken from the 1890 volume of the magazine, *Little Wide-Awake*, which has given its name to this book. Founded in 1875 by Mrs. Lucy Sale Barker it expressed the new spirit abroad. "Little Wide-Awake" was the sobriquet of Mrs. Barker's little boy, and she asked him and the other children what kind of stories they would like for the new periodical. "Let them be about children and dogs and other animals ..." was the reply. "Don't put giants and fairies in". Mr. de Vries evidently shares "Little Wide-Awake's" views. For his selections present much about children, their pets, play, instruction, and everyday interests, but there is little to be found of the prolific fantasy and fairylore of this great era of *Alice* and Andrew Lang.

We are aware all through the volume of the increasing dominance of pictures. These became bolder and larger as the century proceeded, but not always better in quality. A view of the books themselves would show how these also were growing in size, and how varied and attractive were their covers, decorated, gilded, or embossed with pictures on the new book cloth now being used as well as the old paper boards. Alluring covers were essential for sales promotion in these days before book jackets.

Colour printing and chromolithography began to supplant handcoloured illustrations in children's books after the Great Exhibition of 1851, although there had been pioneers in their use, notably the firm of Darton, since 1835 and the firm of Dean & Son were to prolong hand-colouring in their picture-books (represented here by *Wonders of a Toy-Shop*) until well into the 1860s and after. The great picture-book artists of the Victorian era—Walter Crane, Kate Greenaway,—Randolph Caldecott and their famous colour printer, Edmund Evans, are represented only by a few of the delightful illustrations Kate Greenaway made for her own selection from the verses of the Taylor sisters, *Little Anne & Other Poems*. But the excellence of many less famous productions can be observed, especially in the scenes representing a family of children enjoying a holiday in France, depicted by Thomas Crane and Ellen Houghton. This charming picture book, *Abroad*, was one of a series in colour lithography published by Marcus Ward, all presenting children in the everyday world of the early eighties.

Over-emphasis and exaggeration were features of the Victorian age, not only in sadness and sentimentality but in merriment and fun. The yawning child with the candle nicely underlines the trend towards less subtle forms of humour. A rollicking if unrefined vitality characterises the illustrations of Archibald Chasemore, who did a great deal of caricaturish drawing for the magazine *Judy*, and who is represented here by his rendering of the old nursery rhyme, "A Apple Pie". More artistry, if no less exuberance, appears in the pages of *Nursery Nonsense*, where comical drawings by Charles H. Bennett enhance the absurd little rhymes D'Arcy W. Thompson made for "his Baby-boy". In the creations of Lewis Carroll and Edward Lear nonsense in children's books reached its zenith, but in the more ordinary publications of the time laughter soon became guffaws, just as sighs soon became sobs, in this era of violent extremes.

Among so much revealing and interesting

mediocrity it is happy to have some pages from perhaps the best of the many charming nursery rhyme books of the nineteenth century—*Sing-Song*. Christina Rossetti wrote this garland of tender, playful and pensive little verses, "dedicated without permission to the baby who suggested them", perhaps for a little boy she knew, maybe "for a dream child". At first she illustrated the verses herself, but after some attempt to find a suitable artist and a publisher, they were accepted by Routledge in 1871, and Arthur Hughes was selected to illustrate them. At this period, before the introduction of photo-mechanical processes, most of the best book illustration was in black and white, and the woodcuts, engraved by the famous Dalziel brothers, pleased the author, who felt that "they deserved to sell the volume". Of the 121 little songs, riddles and jingles in the original book, Mr. de Vries has selected twenty-four, sufficient to reveal their range of mood and fancy. "Admirable things", wrote Christina's brother, Gabriel Rossetti, to Swinburne, "alternating between the merest babism and a sort of Blakish wisdom and tenderness". Some of the poems can still be found in modern anthologies, but the only complete version, since it was reprinted in 1893 with slight additions, appears to be an American edition published in 1924, with new pictures by Marguerite Davis.

The twilight end of century mood, when the gusto and confidence of Victorianism were fading fast, brought new fancy, delicate whimsy and tender sentiment into children's books. The change is reflected in the pretty trifles, *Songs for Little People*, by Norman Gale, published four years before the new century opened. The "new look" of the nineties is even more strongly expressed in the black and white pictures by Helen Stratton, whose curving line and decorative design reflect the influence of *Art Nouveau* and show the fineness of detail now being made possible by the invention of the photographic line block. There is a kinship with the work of Charles H. Robinson, who had just illustrated a new edition of Stevenson's epoch-making little book, *A Child's Garden of Verses*. "Exquisite and everlasting memorials of a child by no means typical"—commented Gale in his prefatory note to his *Songs*.

A year later—at the end of the Diamond Jubilee year—Gleeson White was to produce the first full-scale survey of children's illustrated books in a special winter number of *The Studio*. This is an important record and assessment of the high artistic achievements of the nineteenth century in children's books. Yet in some ways it gives less real insight into the actual printed and pictorial fare which helped to mould Victorian youth, and so the future of the nation, than these gleanings from more fleeting and forgotten pages, now brought out of oblivion to divert and inform readers for whom they were never intended.

THE MISFORTUNES OF TOBY TICKLEPITCHER

That he threw out poor Toby plump into a ditch.

THE NEST

Come here Jerry Hart, and tell Harry to follow,
   I know where to get at the nest of a swallow;
Up in a corner, behind the old mill;
   The eggs we can eat,—–the hen we can kill;

But the boards they gave way—how very
    provoking!
   Instead of a bird's-nest he got a good
    soaking,
The bird flew away, so Toby ne'er caught her,
   But got in her stead, a fine duck in the
    water.

Toby soon scrambled out, then got in a cart
   With Harry Golightly, and Jeremy Hart;
Then took up the whip—gave the horse such a
    switch

THE BULL DOG

A short time after this, a fierce bull-dog he
    bought,
   Little thinking at that time the tartar he'd
    caught;
He was rough with the neighbours—'A good un
    to fight'
   And not very nice about whom he might
    bite,
One day Master Cæsar [for that was his name]

Seized hold of the leg of a man that was
    lame;
For which a sound thrashing he had to bewail,
    Besides a large saucepan tied fast to his tail.

His courage was great, when put to his metal,
    Which makes it seem strange he should run
      from a kettle;
Yet he did run away—doing mischief until
    He had run up poor Toby a nice little bill.

THE DUMPLINGS

Peggy Thrifty one day bought a charming
    sheep's head,
    With parsley and turnips, and fine wheaten
      bread
To regale her good man when he came home to
    feed,
    But alas! good intentions don't always
      succeed.

For just as she'd peel'd all her turnips and got
    Hard dumplings, with other things nice in
      the pot,
And was tidily laying her white table-cloth,
    Wicked Toby threw quicksilver into her
      broth.

In a very short time the liquor got hot,
    And sheep's head and dumplings jump'd
      from the pot;
Poor Peggy she scream'd—wrung her hands in
    despair,
    When she saw all her cookery dance in the
      air.

THE ARTFUL WOMAN

Dame Cunning went out on a bit of a stroll
    To visit her neighbour, Miss Dorothy Droll;
But as she arrived at Miss Dorothy's door,
    Her eyes they glanced down at a spoon on
      the floor.

'Oh dear!' said the dame 'I am lucky to day,
    Only think now! to find such a prize in my
      way.
Miss Dorothy's drop'd it—it's silver no doubt,
    If I hide it at once, I shall ne'er be found
      out.'

But just as she stoop'd to the place where it lay
    Toby T. pull'd the string, and he snatched
      it away.
'Good lack!' scream'd the dame 'I am sorely
    afraid
    Those two saucy boys must have heard
      what I said.'

THE BROKEN WINDOW

The snow it was deep and frozen each pool
    When Harry and Toby where coming from
      school;
Toby pick'd up a handful, and said [with a grin]
    'I'll give him a snow-ball before he gets in'

Then squeezing it round, took a good aim and
    said,
    'Look out Master Hal for a pat on your
      head;'
But Harry stoop'd down, and let the ball pass

Just over his head, through a large pane of glass.
Toby knew that if caught, there'd be something to pay,
    So ran down the road and was hiding away
When the master came out [old and cunning though slow],
    He traced Toby out by his marks in the snow.

THE FIREWORKS

Hal, Jerry, and Toby were all lazy boys,
    Neglecting their lessons, and breaking their toys;
Not heeding a word that their parents might say,
    But wasting their time in the streets all the day:

Till one fatal eve, they had cause to remember
    Hal's wicked mishap ('twas the fifth of November),
When Jerry bought fireworks—filled both his pockets
    With crackers & blue-lights, squibs, serpents, & rockets.

Hal call'd out to Toby, 'come let's have a lark,'
    Then lighted a paper, and planted a spark
In poor Jerry's pocket, which blazed away
    With such fatal effect, that he died the next day.

TYING THE KNOCKERS

My dear Mrs. Lock, it is useless to knock,
    For I've tried, and I cannot unfasten the lock.
On my word Mr. Moore, I'm not touching your door,
    But some one has fasten'd up mine I am sure.

I don't know what to do, Mr. Moore pray do you,
    I fear that the place is on fire;
I can tell by the noise of the rascally boys
    There is mischief.—Oh how I perspire!

Lawk a daisy! Oh dear! we'll be murder'd I fear,
    When policemen are wanted, they never are near.
Do pray Mr. Moore, burst open the door;
    Or I never shall hear your sweet voice any more.

THE FATAL BRIDGE

The day it was fine, and fair was the tide
    When Toby and Harry determined to ride;
But scarcely had they got their vessel afloat
    Ere they found out that neither could
      manage the boat.

Now though they intended to travel to Kew,
    Their journey was ended before 'twas in
      view;
For Toby not thinking a bridge was so near,
    Ran the head of the boat with such force
      on the pier

That the people above where alarm'd at the
    crash,
    Which was instantly followed by such a
      loud splash!
So sudden the jerk, that ere Toby look'd round,
    Master Harry Golightly, poor fellow! was
      drown'd.

A man who was crying 'Live fowls, doves and
    widgeons,'
    Persuaded our Toby to buy some young
      pigeons.
Who now bought a dove-house, the young ones
    to hatch,
    And a bird-trap, to see if some more he
      could catch.

Then out from the garret, he mounted aloof,
    And fix'd up his pigeon-house high on the
      roof,
Where a bird getting out, and beginning to

flutter,
    Was follow'd by Toby o'er roof, tiles, and
      gutter

Till his fatal mishap, how I tremble to tell!
    Master Toby's foot slip'd, to the pavement
      he fell;
His mother came out, full of grief, and there
    found
    Her unfortunate boy lying dead on the
      ground.

SLOW POISON

'*There is death in the pot.*'

The leaves have forsaken the trees,
    The sloe bush is naked and bare,
The Hysons, Souchongs and Boheas
    Are only sloe poison I fear.

THE BOY'S WEEK-DAY BOOK

It was on a dark winter's night, when the wind whistled aloud, and the flakes of snow fell fast against the window panes, that William Brown was sorting his library books, and Alfred and Henry, his brothers, were seated at a table covered with green baize, and spread over with books suitable for young people.

The boys began to talk freely about their books, and their uncle Jones joined in their conversation.

'I have often thought,' said he, 'that if I were to write a book, it should be called THE BOY'S WEEK-DAY BOOK; and I do think I could make it worth a boy's attention.'

Before he said this, he had been examining the books on the table; each of them had something good in it, though none of them were exactly suited to his taste. One had, he thought, too many pictures in it; another had no picture at all; one was very entertaining, but not serious; another was serious, but not interesting or entertaining; and he knew very well, that young people require a mixture of the grave and the gay to edify them ...

He thus addressed his nephews:—The great object of every human being is happiness. Now, as experience has abundantly proved, that no one can be happy who does not fear God, and perform the duties which he owes to his fellow creatures, so THE BOY'S BOOK ought to teach young people to fear God, and to do their duty to their fellow creatures, that they may be hap-

py. This is an observation so plain, and so reasonable, that I think none will be found to contradict it. It is true, that many people appear to be happy, who neither fear God, nor perform their duties to those around them; but their enjoyment is of short duration, it is not that abiding happiness which we all wish to obtain. If a boy play truant by keeping away from school, he may, for an hour or two, be tolerably happy; but then comes upon him the fear of punishment, and he has to return, at last, to suffer shame, and pain, and disgrace. If a poor man spend what money he has in drink, he may feel happy for a short time among his drunken companions; but in the morning he has to endure the head-ache, sickness, reproach, and poverty. This is not happiness.

Again; if an ungodly man be happy in his life, what are his prospects in death? His end is hopeless, and when he dies eternal misery is his portion. Can this deserve the name of happiness? It is of little use to be happy for a short season, if we thereby render ourselves miserable for a long one. THE BOY'S BOOK should teach youth how to be happy in life, death, and eternity. The great difficulty in writing a *Boy's Book* is to make it cheerful without encouraging thoughtlessness, and serious without creating disgust. It should be a pleasant mixture of the lively and the serious; of pastime and study; of light-heartedness and reflection. A boy should not spin his peg-top from morning to night, nor pore over his book for ever ...

In writing THE BOY'S BOOK there is one great point which has been constantly kept in view, and that is, the close connexion existing between youth and manhood, time and eternity.

THE FIRST CHAPTER

And in that feeble frame distinctly scan
The infant image of the future man.

How hard it is to imagine, when we look on a helpless infant smiling in the arms of its mother, or sleeping in its crib or cradle, that its little heart will soon burn with anger, its dimpled cheeks redden with rage, and its mild blue eyes sprakle with evil passions! How difficult it is to persuade ourselves, that those waxen lips, through which the softly breathing sigh is scarcely heard to pass, will become loud and clamorous, and utter sinful thoughts, and wicked words! And yet, if we look around us, we must be convinced that, at a very early age, the bad passions of the heart begin to show themselves, and require every care to subdue them. Well may parents watch and pray over their tender offspring, that they may not be led into temptation, but be delivered from evil, and guided in their pilgrimage from earth to heaven.

Memory, in after years, often goes back to the spot where infancy enjoyed its sports, and endured its little troubles. I can yet remember the

play-place of my infancy, and the school-room where I and my playmates learned our A B C as we

'Sat on a bench all-a-row.'

Nor have I forgotten the corner, where, at times, I stood on a form, sobbing and blubbering with the dunce's cap on my head, and the rod in my hand, while my old schoolmistress, with her spectacles on her nose, sat in the great arm-chair, scolding and mending stockings. Here, my lads, is a drawing I have made, from a recollection of scenes which will never be effaced from my memory.

It is a delightful thing to see good children cheerful and happy, either in town or country, at home or at school, in winter or in summer, even if it is only in flying a kite.

For all good boys and girls may play
In proper time, and place, and way.

But it is a thing still more delightful, to see them going on in the way to heaven, trusting in Jesus Christ, prizing the Bible, honouring their parents, obeying their teachers, loving their companions, and growing in grace, and in the knowledge of divine things.

THE SECOND CHAPTER

A father once rebuked his cruel children in the following manner. He told them that he had some very heavy charges to bring against them, and that the complainants whom they had injured were all waiting in the next room, and would appear against them. The children were much frightened at this, and begged hard to

18

know what they were charged with. Their father told them that one complainant had been pushed by them into a puddle up to his knees; another wounded by a sharp spike; a third knocked down; a fourth stoned; a fifth robbed of all that his house contained; and a sixth frightened almost out of his senses. All the children denied the truth of these accusations, and declared that they had never been guilty of such cruelty in their lives; but their father told them, he could not believe them, for that children who were cruel, would not scruple to tell falsehoods. He then fetched a basket from the next room, and placed it on the table. Uncovering the basket, he took out a poor fly, which one of them had wantonly pushed into a cup of treacle; a cockchafer, which they had been spinning; a butterfly, which they had knocked down as he was flying over the garden; a frog, whose leg they had broken with a stone, as he hopped about by the side of a pond; and a bird's nest, with the eggs they had taken from it. He then went out, and returned with a dog, to whose tail they had cruelly tied an old tin kettle, which rattled against the ground as he ran, and drove him almost mad. The children were all confounded. Their father explained to them, that if they had committed those acts of cruelty towards their fellow creatures, they would have been severely punished; but that their wickedness was not less clearly shown by being committed against feeble and helpless creatures, which had power neither to defend themselves, nor to punish their tormentors. They cried while their father spoke of the bird's nest; and he succeeded in convincing them of the sin which they had committed; and though the punishment he inflicted was light compared with their cruelty, it impressed on their youthful minds the remembrance of their transgression, and they did not again practise cruelty ... It is better to overcome evil in youth, than to let it overcome us in manhood.

Pull the weeds up while they are young,
Lest their roots grow stout and strong.

There is every encouragement to young persons, if they persevere steadily in acquiring good habits, and avoiding bad ones. When a boy first begins his A B C, it is very hard work for a short time, yet by degrees he gets over it, and begins to read! And, then, what a pleasure to be able to read a good and a pleasant book! Oh, it is worth while to go through the trouble of learning to read fifty times over, to obtain the advantage of reading the Bible. There are many good books, but none like the Bible.

A wayward and disobedient child brings not only sorrow on others, but also on himself. A wilful lad once wandered where he was told never to go, and in scrambling to the top of a hedge, to get some bright red and yellow berries which had caught his eye, his clothes were torn by the brambles, and a dozen sharp thorns broke in his fingers. He gathered some of the berries, and ate them; but, finding them ill tasted, he gathered no more, and well it was for him that he did not, for the berries were poison. He returned home to be punished for his disobedience, sick at his stomach, his clothes torn, and his bleeding fingers smarting with pain. A day or

two after, when walking out with his father, he saw at a little distance an idle, dirty, miserable-looking boy, whom a farmer was flogging for stealing. 'Father! father!' said he, 'look, yonder is a boy who has been gathering poison berries!' The lad was right, for every one who does wrong gathers poison berries, and the thorns of reproach will not only stick in his fingers, but in his heart. It has been said that the heaviest burdens are those which we lay upon ourselves, and the sharpest thorns those of our own planting; and it is equally true, that

The young who in wisdom and virtue
    engage,
Lay up comfort for manhood, and peace
    for old age.

THE THIRD CHAPTER

'Mid sterner care's engrossing power,
   How sweet it is, surpassing measure.
To witness childhood's buoyant hour
   Of happiness and guiltless pleasure.

Writing 'THE BOY'S BOOK', is a little like making up medicine for a naughty child, when the silly fellow wishes more sugar than is good for him. If you make it too sweet, it may do him no good; and if not sweet enough, the urchin is very unwilling to take it at all. Most young people think that 'a bird in the hand is worth two in the bush;' and, indeed, this is pretty much the case in all the stages of life. The child chooses a sugar plum to-day, rather than a plum cake to-morrow. The boy prefers the sport which gives present pleasure, to the study that promises future advantage; and the man grasps the good things of this world, in preference to those of the world which is to come. The young and the old, the wise and the foolish agree, that as life is short, we should make the most of it; but there is a great difference in the way and manner in which they proceed to make the most of it. The young pursue pleasure; the old, riches and reputation. A good man beautifully describes the manner in which he wished to make the most of life:—

'Live while you live,' the epicure would
   say,
'And seize the pleasures of the present day.'
'Live while you live,' the sacred preacher
   cries,

'And give to God each moment as it
   flies.'—
Lord, in my view let both united be;
I live in pleasure, while I live to thee.

When gazing on the rosy train,
   All noisy, happy, wild,
My heart beats faster, and again
   I wish myself a child.

It is a pleasant sight to see the young play with those of their own age at *tick*, *puss in the corner*, *ring-taw*, and *hot beans ready buttered;* and in these boyish amusements much self-denial and good-nature may be practised. This, however, is not always the case, for sometimes cruelty, tyranny, and oppression are as much at work in the breast of a schoolboy, as they ever were in the bosom of a Dey of Algiers.

Bill Gruby was a lad of a very domineering

spirit. Every other boy was compelled by him to do just what he pleased. If a band of little boys were playing at *hop-scotch, marbles, trap and ball*, or carrying stones with *the leathern sucker*, 'Gruby is coming!' was the signal to snatch up the marbles, the ball, and the sucker, otherwise none of them would have been secure. There was scarcely a boy in the school who had not suffered from the tyranny of Gruby.

THE FOURTH CHAPTER

What a variety of games there are wherein boys can find innocent amusement! and, yet, how few things are more common than mischievous and cruel diversions! When young people delight in dog-fighting, tormenting cats, beating donkeys, throwing at birds, or in ridiculing the infirmities of other boys, or of old people, it is a proof that there is something bad at work within them. *Skipping*, and *peg-top*, and *trap and ball* and *leap-frog*, and *prison-base*, and *flying kites*,

and *marbles*, and *sliding*, and twenty other games, afford excellent pastime, without having recourse to folly, wickedness, and cruelty. Why should the stream of life be poisoned at the fountain! Why should youth be tainted with principles and practices which will hang heavy on the heart of age!

> How sweet is the springtide of life, when the eye
> Is lit up like the sunbeam that lightens the sky;
> When the heart and the pleasures around it agree,
> And the hope is as fresh as the leaf on the tree!
> In manhood a thousand vexations annoy,
> But the blithest of pleasures is known by the boy,
> When he runs with delight at his schoolfellow's call
> To his kite, and his peg-top, his hoop, and his ball.

To see young people happy, is, indeed, a pleasant sight, but only so when their pastimes are free from what is evil; for the happiness of to-day is bought at too dear a price, if to be paid for with remorse to-morrow.

Great is the advantage which young persons may gain from habits of intimacy with aged people, particularly among the pious poor. There are no events of my boyish days which I review with more pleasure than the errands of mercy on which my parents sent me. To read a chapter of the Bible to the untaught, to run on an errand for the lame, to sit by the sick bed of the afflicted, or to give a penny to a blind man, is in the power of most young persons; and such employments are blessings to those who practise them, as well as to those who are benefited by them. There is a peace within, and a glory around that cottage where God is worshipped with sincerity; and, to relieve the wants, to add to the comforts, and to soften the sorrows of the aged disciples of Christ, is a privilege which every young person should seek to obtain. And who can say how many blessings the benevolent are indebted for to the prayers of the objects of their bounty?

Never shall I forget the figure of an old man

whom I saw in my boyish days, as he sat in the chimney corner of a cottage, lifting up his hands towards his gray hairs in the very spirit of thankfulness to God, repeating the words—

'Through all the changing scenes of life,
    In trouble and in joy,
The praises of my God shall still
    My heart and tongue employ.

'Of his deliverance I will boast,
    Till all that are distrest,
From my example comfort take,
    And charm their griefs to rest.'

THE FIFTH CHAPTER

These youngsters, thoughtless as they now
    appear,
Will be the gray-beards of some future year.

Where is the boy, who has ever left his parents to attend a boarding-school, who has forgotten the first moment when he entered the school-house? When a boy quits his home for the first time to dwell among strangers, it is a dark day to him. In vain have his father and mother told him, that he will have plenty of pleasant play-fellows, and may be as happy as a little king. In vain does his father, as he accompanies him to school, attempt to cheer him, by talking of the holidays that will soon come round. There is a dismal foreboding of long lessons and unknown punishments, and the young urchin is consigned to his schoolmaster, with about as much cheerfulness in his face, and happiness in his heart, as if he were placed under the care of a jailor. He

struggles hard to keep up appearances, while his father tells him to be a good boy, and takes his leave. In vain his new playfellows gather round him; in vain he fumbles in his pocket for the new shilling given him by his mother; in vain is the play-ground extended before him; neither comrades, nor shillings, nor play-ground can banish the feeling of desolation that has gathered round his heart. He wanders into a by-lane, gets behind a tree, and bursts into tears. But

'The tear down childhood's cheek that
    flows
Is like the dew-drop on the rose,
For when the summer breeze comes by
And waves the bush, the flower is dry.'

What a contrast to this gloomy season is the

22

time of *breaking up for the holidays!* ... This is a red ink day, and a joyous night in a schoolboy's life. He fears neither tasks nor punishments; the notches that recorded the days he had to remain at school, have all disappeared, and the very stick on which they were cut has been thrown away in the frolics of wayward pleasure. Home, and all that is dear to him, is present to his thoughts; and he is brave enough to look even on the face of his schoolmaster without fear.

The morning comes! the happy morn when he leaves the school. He is up betimes. If it be winter, it is a glorious frost, and the frozen snow crackles beneath the tread delightfully. If it be summer, the sun is bright in the skies, and the roads are dusty. The caravan arrives, which is to carry away his boxes, and, at last, are heard the rattling wheels of the coach or chaise destined to bear him home. The steps are let down, and he scarcely feels them as he mounts into the vehicle with his companions. Smack goes the whip; round go the wheels; some wave their hats, or the flags they have prepared for the purpose; never so much as looking at the finger post that points out the road. Away scamper the horses, and away go, too, a throng of exulting hearts as happy as ever beat in human bosoms.

THE SIXTH CHAPTER

Lull'd in my mother's lap of love,
  My earlier moments were beguiled;
How did my wayward childhood rove
  While all around me pleasure smiled!
But yet methought some brighter joy
Would greet me when a bigger boy.

One of my early playmates was a mouse-catcher,

and very expert he became in this calling. Another was skilful enough occasionally to secure a rat. I can fancy that I am now going, with the companions of my childhood, our accustomed round, to examine the *mole-traps*, set by the village mole-catcher. Here are heaps of fresh earth newly turned up by the little burrowers under ground. There! the bended stick has sprung up, and the poor mole is hung up by the neck, his little eyes buried in the depth of the soft fur of his skin, and his little feet, just like human hands, white and fingered, are spread as if supplicating for mercy. He hangs in the air as a terror to evil doers; but, unfortunately for the poor moles under ground, they cannot profit by the death of their companion, for they cannot witness the example that has been made of him.

THE SEVENTH CHAPTER

As the hours of his boyhood to virtue are given;
As he leaves what is sinful, and seeks after

23

The different habits and dispositions of boys are constantly showing themselves in the little events of the day. I shall not soon forget Jeffries, a cruel schoolfellow of mine, who, having robbed a poor bird of her young ones, drove a nail through one of them, and fastened it to a barn door, and, then, threw the remaining unfledged little ones into a pond, to be gobbled up by the ducks. Dalton fought with him about it; for though Jeffries was much the bigger and stronger boy, Dalton abhorred his cruelty too much to witness it without a struggle in defence of the poor birds. I recollect my mother once caught me with a bird's-nest full of eggs, which I had taken from the hedge; she took me to my father, who gave me such a sharp and just reproof for robbing the poor birds as I shall never forget.

heaven; —
So the years of his age will be blessed or
    forlorn,
And plant in his bosom a rose or a thorn.

THE EIGHTH CHAPTER

Seek the guidance of God, then, while
    time's on the wing,
Lest the winter of life nip the bud of the
    spring;
Let pleasures eternal thy moments engage,
Lest the joys of thy youth prove the grief
    of thine age.

William Bowers was of a disposition the very reverse of that of Jeffries. Many are the years which have passed away since he buried his sky-lark, but I have not forgotten it. He made a coffin of painted pasteboard; dug the grave in the corner of his little garden, and set up a piece of deal board, neatly cut, for a tomb-stone. I remember that when he wrote the inscription on the board, the ink ran sadly, so that one letter appeared to join another, but, for all that, it looked very pretty.

THE NINTH CHAPTER

'Take heed to thy ways,' Father Donald
    would say,
   'For guilt is succeeded by sorrow;

Then haste thee, my son, from
    temptations away,
Lest the sin that procures thee the joy of
    to-day,
    Should fill thee with anguish to-morrow.'

In more places than one in THE BOY'S BOOK, young people are urged to learn to do those things well which they are most frequently called upon to perform. If this observation were more generally attended to, the good effects would be very extensive. Every boy should endeavour to speak *distinctly*. This is of as much use as speaking according to the rules of grammar. Many boys, and indeed men also, are so careless in this respect, that they are almost always obliged to repeat their expressions before they are understood. A little fellow at a house where I dined the other day, was desired to ask a blessing: this he did; but if he had mumbled it over in the dialect of the Cherokee Indian, it would have been quite as well understood: not one syllable could I comprehend, though his mother called him a good boy for his performance! The use of speech is to convey our ideas one to another, but if the words are not understood, the sounds are of no more use than if a poker and fireshovel were struck against each other.

    Whether you whisper low, or loudly call,
    Distinctly speak, or never speak at all.

Swimming is one of the most agreeable recreations of boys and lads, and it may happen to prove very useful. It would be well if every person learned to swim, for instances are continually occurring of persons being drowned, whose

lives might be spared by the timely assistance of swimmers. None but those who have felt it can tell the misery of seeing another drowned without possessing the power of rendering any succour. In my youth I underwent this trial, and it made such an impression on my mind, that I determined never again to endure it, if learning to swim well would enable me to avoid it. I saw the head and the flowing hair of the drowning person within a few yards of me, but the water was deep, and the current was strong, and I durst not venture to leap from the bank, which was several feet above the river. In another min-

ute it was too late. This occurrence affected me in my dreams, and disturbed my slumbers, for I felt like a culprit who, by cowardice, had allowed another to perish.

    Few persons given to reflection can gaze on the rising sun without being insensibly drawn to the thought of the amazing power of his Almighty Maker; and the wide expanded heavens, arrayed with so many bright and glowing colours, increase the impression made upon the mind.

    If thus the sky above our head,
    Which God beneath his feet has spread,
    With floods of living light excels;
    What must the heaven be where he dwells!

It would be difficult to say which of all boyish

games affords the greatest degree of amusement, for whether boys are engaged at *hop-step-and-jump*, *bait the bear*, or *drawing the oven;* whether they are at full speed at *hare and hounds, stag-warning*, or in *running races*, they appear equally happy. A good game at *cricket* is an excellent amusement for grown boys, and when the bowler and batsman are good players, and the rest possess a tolerable degree of skill, it is full of exercise and interest. For myself, I do not know that I have ever enjoyed any game so much as a good thorough set-to at *snowballing*. A boy feels,

when engaged in this game, that he has something to endure, and this gives a tone of elevation to his mind. There is a sort of bravery, a kind of heroism necessary to stand his ground well, amid the peltings of his companions; and if a boy have any heart within him, he will not let a handful of cold snow frighten him from the field.

THE TENTH CHAPTER

I loved Father Donald, for oft when a
    child,
  On his knee I've been happy at night,
While his bosom was glad, and his
    countenance smiled,
  And his tongue with a tale my rapt fancy
    beguiled,
  And filled my young heart with delight.

THE TWELFTH CHAPTER

And now, reader, THE BOY'S WEEK-DAY BOOK is drawing to a close. It has pointed out what you have been, what you are, and what you ought to be. It has reproved folly and vice: it has commended wisdom and virtue. It has endeavoured to amuse and instruct you, and to excite in your heart a disposition to avoid all that is evil, and

to attain every thing which is good... It has laid before you examples to avoid, and to imitate. It has shown that the happiness of the man depends on the good conduct of the boy, and that the prospect of heaven is cleared or clouded, by the actions done on earth. In conclusion, I would
    'Commit both thee and it unto that Hand
    That pulls the strong down, and makes
        weak ones stand:'
even to Him who in boundless compassion has not withheld his only Son from offering up himself a sacrifice for sin, that we might not perish, but have eternal life.

The reading of THE BOY'S BOOK was not intended to affect you like a puppet-show, which excites a momentary pleasure, and is then forgotten; but, rather, like a summer evening's landscape, wherein the setting sun, the gliding clouds, the whispering breeze, the waving tree, the singing bird, and the babbling brook, not only communicate pleasure, but, at the same time, lead the heart,
    'Mid earth, and skies, and wood, and
        waterfall,
    To Him whose boundless goodness gave
        them all.'

If no error has been repressed, and no virtuous affection excited or encouraged in your heart, THE BOY'S WEEK-DAY BOOK has been written in vain; but if it has made you ashamed of what is mean, and unworthy, and wicked; and given birth to aught that is generous and noble in desire, and pure and useful in practice; if it has disposed you to humility of heart, and integrity of purpose; if it has taught you to fear God, and to be useful in your generation; and, above all, if it has shown you that you can only be saved by faith in Christ, and only be good as you are guided by the Holy Spirit, then has its object been attained, and its pages, with all their feebleness and faults, have been more highly honoured than if they had been printed in letters of gold...

THE TURNER

Joe Steady is clever and quick at his trade,
    You may plainly discern, by the things he
      has made:
The boy's as they pass, stop and peep in his
  shop,
    To admire how nicely he turns out a top.

THE ENGINEER

Come along Master Gray, let's be off for the day,
    The steam it is up, and is puffing away;
Our cares we can lighten at Windsor or
  Brighton,
    The distance is great, and there's little to
      pay.

So rapid the pace, no horse in a race
    Could equal the speed of our train;
How frightfully fast the other trains past.
    I wish we were safe out again.

Thus on railways we fly (or at least very nigh),
    Few birds on the wing can go faster;
With a staunch Engineer there is nothing to
  fear
    Except now and then a disaster.

THE BLACK-SMITH

The bellows roar, the fire burns,
    The Smiths their hammers raise in turns;
The Iron then begins to show
    A different shape at every blow.
Useful in every form it takes,
    Horses shoes, ploughs, spades, or rakes;
In short, for *use* we are truely told
    That Iron far surpasses gold.

THE MASON

The rough-hewn stone is chisel'd round,
    And firmly fixed on solid ground;
A base just fit to place King Lud's son,
    Our George the fourth, or Ex-king Hudson:

Or tawdry house where members play
    And fool the nation's cash away,
Where not a gallery, stair, or room
    Is what it should be—ask Lord Brougham.

Where, what's within, the outside tells
    By sundry lots of caps and bells;
Where, ere the inside's fit for hearing,
    The outside *Nobs* will want repairing.

THE BAKER

With basket at back, no labour he grudges,
    But whistles and sings, while onward he
    trudges
Through hail, rain, or snow, or sultry hot
  weather;
    His pride is 'To keep his connection
    together.'

To the mistress a bow—a smile to the maid—
    Doughy knows pretty well how to manage
    his trade;
Extols the girl's beauty while a loaf she is
  taking,
    Then tells her what care he will take of her
    baking;

Asks her to buy a few biscuits, or cakes,
    Proclaiming what beautiful french bread
    he bakes;
Thus Doughy goes on with a good word to all,
    His face it is welcome where 'ere he may
    call.

THE BRICKLAYER

The ground is marked out—the foundation
  laid—
    The piers are run up—the openings made—
The arches are turned—the flooring joists
  fix'd—
    The chimneys are planned—the mortar all
    mix'd—

Now a high scaffold built, as they raise up the
wall—
    The labourers skulk—the bricklayers call
'Paddy, more mortar—Paddy more bricks
    We have used them all up and are quite in
        a fix,'

'Coming! coming!' says Paddy 'if a moment
    you'll stop,
    This ladder's a very long way to the top.'
Then shoots down his load, and scratching his
nob,
    Says 'A few courses more will finish the
        job.

THE CARPENTER

The joiner comes in when the bricklayer leaves,
    Pulls off his jacket—tucks up his sleeves—
Draws out his plans—sharpens each tool—
    Then measures his work with his little
        joint rule,
To see how much stuff each portion will take,
    A window—a cupboard—or staircase to
        make;
Then mortices neatly the framing of doors,
    And planes up the stuff for panels and
        floors;

Till at last he comes down to the kitchen below,
    Where a dresser he fixes, and shelves in a
        row;
With a bench underneath for the saucepans to
lay,
    Then lets in the painter, and toddles away.

THE PAINTER

Will Putty comes last in the House-building
    Trade,
    And beautifies all that the others have
        made;
He stops up the cracks, and cleans off each
    splinter.
    Preserving the wood from rough weather
        in winter.

With diamond cut glass then he fits in each
    pane,
    Puts pipes, spouts, and gutters to carry off
        rain;
Scrapes the rust off of iron-work, knockers and
    railings,
    And hides with his brush, the other men's
        failings.

Lays on the water, the cisterns he fixes,
    For graining the front, then the colour he
        mixes,
With a nice coat of varnish its finished at last,
    Then his tools he packs up and makes the
        door fast.

THE COOPER

The Cooper retails foot baths, pails,
    Barrels, hogsheads, butts, and firkins;
Tubs for mashing, cooling, washing,
    Bathing, pickling meat or gherkins:

He also shaves and bends his staves,
    The monstrous spirit vat to build;

Then iron bound and hoop'd all round
　　With fine OLD TOM 'tis fill'd.

This done, he tries the vessel's size,
　　And then in figures bold;
Declares it will if you it fill,
　　Five hundred gallons hold.

THE BASKET-MAKER

With supple wands and nimble hands
　　I labour at my trade;

Some round, some square, I make my ware,
　　And better can't be made.

My osiers dry I firmly tie
　　For market, fruit, or clothes;
'Who'll buy! who'll buy! come ladies try
　　And purchase one of Joe's?'

If once you deal, I'm sure you'll feel
　　You've not been doing wrong,
Though small my gains, I take great pains
　　To make them neat and strong.

BOB THE CABIN-BOY AND HIS CAPTAIN

A FEW MONTHS since, a vessel sailed from England, with a captain, whose habitual blasphemy, drunkenness, and tyranny, so disgusted the crew, that some of the most fatal consequences might have taken place, but for the sudden and alarming illness of their cruel and depraved commander. The mate took charge of the ship, and the captain, greatly afflicted in his cabin, was left, by the unanimous voice of a hardened crew, to perish. He had continued nearly a week in this neglected state, no one venturing to visit him, when the heart of a poor boy on board was touched with his sufferings, and he determined to enter the cabin and speak to him. He descended the companion-ladder, and opening the state-room door, called out, 'Captain, how are you?' A surly voice replied, 'What's that to you?—be off.' Next morning, however, he went down again—'Captain, hope you are better.' 'Oh, Bob, I'm very bad—been very ill all night.' 'Captain, please to let me wash your hands and face; it will refresh you very much.' The captain nodded assent. Having performed this kind office, the boy said, 'Please, Master, let me shave you.' He was permitted to do this also; and having adjusted the bed-clothes, he grew bolder, and proposed some tea. The captain knew he had no mercy to expect from his crew, and had determined not to solicit any; 'I'll perish,' said his obstinate, perverse soul, 'rather than ask one favour of them.' But the kindness of this poor boy found its way to his heart; and, in spite of all his daring, independent spirit, his bowels melted, and his iron face displayed the starting tear.

The captain now declined apace: his weakness

was daily increasing, and he became gradually convinced that he should not live many weeks at farthest. His mind was filled with increasing terror as the prospect of death and eternity drew nearer to his confused and agitated view. He was as ignorant as he was wicked. Brought up among the worst of seamen in early life, he had imbibed all their principles, followed their practices, and despised remonstrance or reproof, A man-of-war had finished his education; and a long course of successful voyages, as master of a vessel, had contributed to harden his heart, and led him not only to say, 'there is no God,' but to act under that persuasion. Alarmed at the idea of death, and ignorant of the way of salvation, with a conscience now thundering conviction to his guilty soul, he cried one morning, just as Bob opened the state-room door, and affectionately inquired, 'Well, Master, how is it with you this morning?'—'Ah, Bob, I'm very bad; my body is getting worse and worse; but I should not mind that so much, were it not for my soul. Oh, Bob, what shall I do? I'm a great sinner. I'm afraid I shall go to hell—I deserve it. Alas, Bob, I'm a lost man.' 'Oh, no, Master,' said the boy, 'Jesus Christ can save you.' 'No, Bob, no, I cannot see the least prospect of being saved. Oh, what a sinner I have been! what will become of me?' His stony heart was broken, and he poured out his complaints before the boy, who strove all he could to comfort him, but in vain.

One morning the boy just appeared, when the captain sung out, 'Oh Bob, I've been thinking of a Bible. I know there is not one in the cabin; go forward and see if you can find one in the men's chests.' The boy succeeded, and the poor dying man beheld him enter with tears of joy. 'Ah! Bob, that will do—that will do; you must read to me, and I shall soon know whether such a wicked man as I am can be saved, and how it is to be done. Now, Bob, sit down on my chest, and read to me out of that blessed book.' 'Where shall I read, Master?' 'I do not know, Bob. I never read it myself; but try and pick out some places that speak about *sinners* and *salvation*.' 'Well, Master, then I'll take the New Testament; you and I shall understand it better; for, as my poor mother used to say, there are not so many hard words there.' The boy read for two hours, while the captain, stretching his neck over the bed-place, listened with the eagerness of a man on the verge of eternity. Every word conveyed light to his mind, and his astonished soul soon beheld sin as he had never seen it before. The justice of God in his eternal ruin

struck him with amazing force; and, though he heard of a Saviour, still the great difficulty of knowing how *he* could be saved, appeared a mystery unfathomable. He had been ruminating a great part of the night on some passages Bob had read, but they only served to depress his spirits, and terrify his soul.

The next morning, when the boy entered the state-room, he exclaimed, 'Oh, Bob, I shall never live to reach the land. I am dying very fast; you'll soon have to cast me overboard; but all this is nothing—my soul, my poor soul! Ah, Bob, my dear lad, what will become of my soul? Oh, I shall be lost for ever. Can't you pray?' 'No, Master, I never prayed in my life, any more than the Lord's Prayer my mother taught me.' 'Oh, Bob, pray for me; go down on your knees and cry for mercy; do, Bob, God will bless you for it. Oh, kneel down and pray for your poor wicked captain.' The boy hesitated—the master urged—the lad wept—the master groaned, 'God be merciful to me a sinner!' Both cried greatly. 'Oh, Bob, for God's sake, kneel down and pray for me.' Overcome by importunity and compassion, the boy fell on his knees, and with heavy sobs, cried out, 'O Lord, have mercy on my poor dying captain! O Lord, I am a poor, ignorant, wicked sailor-boy. Lord, I don't know what to say. Lord, the captain says I must pray for him, but I don't know how. Lord, have mercy on him. He says he shall be lost—Lord, save him! He says he shall go to hell—Lord, take him to heaven! He says he shall be with devils— oh, that he may be with angels! Don't let him perish, O Lord! Thou knowest I love him, and am sorry he is so ill. The men won't come near him, but I'll do the best I can for him as long as he lives; but I can't save him. O Lord, pity my poor captain; see how thin and how weak he is! Oh, comfort his troubled mind! Oh, help me, Lord, to pray for my master.' The captain was too much affected to speak. The simplicity, sincerity, and humility of the lad's prayer had so much impressed his mind, that he lay groaning inwardly with spiritual anguish, and wetting his couch with tears. Bob retired on deck, for the scene had quite overcome him. In the evening he again read the Bible to the captain, whose soul appeared to receive every word with indescribable eagerness. The next morning, on entering the state-room, the boy was struck with the extraordinary change visible in his master's features. That gloomy horror which had so long added to the natural ferocity of his weather-beaten coutenance was fled; and while his afflictions had softened and more fully exhibited the various parts of his countenance, the circumstance of the past night had settled the whole arrangement of his features into a holy, pleasant, calm and resigned state, that would seem to say, An heir of grace can 'find glory begun below.'

'Oh, Bob, my dear lad,' said the captain, with great humility, 'I have had such a night! After you left me I fell into a sort of dose; my mind was full of the many blessed things you had been reading to me from the precious Bible. All on a sudden I thought I saw, in that corner of my bed-place, Jesus Christ, hanging bleeding on his cross. Struck with the idea, I thought I arose and crawled to the place, and casting myself at his feet in the greatest agony of soul, I cried out for a long time, like the blind man you read of, 'Jesus, thou Son of David, have mercy on me.' At length I thought he looked on me. Yes, my dear lad, he looked at your poor wicked captain; and oh, Bob, what a look it was! I shall never forget it. My blood rushed to my heart—my pulse beat high—my soul thrilled with agitation, and, waiting for him to speak, with fear not unmixed with hope, I saw him smile. Oh, my child, I saw him smile—yes, and he smiled on *me*—on *me*, Bob. Oh, my dear boy, he smiled on wretched guilty me. Ah, what did I feel at that moment! My heart was too full to speak; but I waited, and ventured to look up, when I heard him say, hanging as he did on the cross, the blood streaming from his hands, and feet, and side—oh, Bob, what sounds were these!—shall I ever hear his beloved voice again?—I heard him say, in sounds that angels cannot reach, "*Son, be of good cheer; thy sins, which be many, are all forgiven thee!*" My heart burst with joy; I fell prostrate at his feet; could not utter a word but glory, glory, glory! The vision vanished; I fell back on my pillow; I opened my eyes; I was covered with perspiration, I said, "Oh, this cannot be a dream!" No, Bob, I know that Jesus bled and died for me; I can believe the promises —the many precious promises you have read to me out of the Bible, and I feel that the blood of the cross can cleanse even *me*. I am not now afraid to die; no, Bob, my sins are pardoned through Jesus. I want no more; I am now ready to die; I have no wish to live. I cannot—I feel I cannot be many days longer on this side of eternity. The extreme agitation of my mind, of late, has increased the fever of my body, and I shall soon breathe my last.' The boy who had silently shed many tears, now burst into a flood of sorrow, and involuntarily cried, 'No, my dear Master, don't leave me.' 'Bob,' said he, calmly, 'my dear boy, comfort your mind; I am happy—I am going to be happy for ever. I feel for you as if you were my own child. I am sorry to leave you in such a wicked world, and with such wicked men as sailors are in general. Oh, may you ever be kept from those crimes into which I have fallen. Your kindness to me, my dear lad, has been great; God will reward you for it. To you I owe every thing as an instrument in the Lord's hands. Surely He sent you to me! God bless you, my dear boy; tell my crew to forgive me, as I forgive and pray for them.' Thus the day passed in the most pleasing and profitable manner, when Bob, after reading the Bible as usual, retired to his hammock. Eager the next morning to meet again, Bob arose at day-light, and opening the state-room door, saw his master had risen from his pillow, and crawled to the corner of his bed-place, where, in his dream, he beheld the cross. There he appeared kneeling down in the attitude of prayer, his hands clasped and raised, and his body leaning against the ship-side. The boy paused, and waited a few moments, fearful of disturbing his master. At length he called, in a sort of whisper, 'Master.' No answer. 'Master.' No reply. He ventured to creep forward a little, and then said, 'Master.' All was silent! Again he cried, 'Captain.' Silence reigned. He stretched out his hand and touched his leg; it was cold, and stiff, and clammy. He called again, 'Captain.' He raised his hand to his shoulder; he tenderly shook it. The position of the body was altered; it declined gently until it rested on the bed; but the spirit had fled some hours before, we hope, to be with Christ, which is far better.

THE BLIND FIDDLER.

Old John Groggins, the blind fiddler, brings his beggar-dog, and plays the Old Hundredth and other Psalm tunes every Saturday night, at the corner of the quiet street, next door but one to the Misses Crotchey, who declare that they must remove to a less musical street.

AFFECTING ACCOUNT OF A LITTLE BOY, WHO WAS KILLED IN INDIA, BY A MAD DOG

I WILL offer to your notice a very interesting account of a Little Boy who was, in his earliest infant days, blessed with the superintending care of a pious mother, who had learnt to know that the almighty God was a refuge in the hour of calamity, and his word a sure support. Strange, but delightful sight! to behold a child of five years of age, so thoroughly aware of the truth of the Bible, and so experimentally alive to its promises.

He was playing at his father's door, with his bearer, when a large dog passing by, fiercely attacked him, seized hold of his cheek, and inflicted a severe and ghastly wound, the fangs of the brute entering into the child's mouth: medical aid was obtained, and the wound gradually healed; and there seemed no further evil consequences to be apprehended. About a month subsequent to this misfortune, the poor little fellow was affected, as his affectionate mother supposed, with only a common fever, and medicine was, in consequence, administered; but on the following day, some spasmodic difficulty was perceptible on the child's attempting to drink water; these symptoms were removed by medicine, and he appeared better, and in good spirits. About twelve o'clock at night, the surgeon, who slept by his side, observed an alarming recurrence of the unfavourable symptoms, the urgency of which had been temporarily relieved by leeches. At five the following morning, the poor little patient fell into dreadful paroxysms, shortly after leaving the hot bath, and seemed like one making plunging efforts to escape drowning, crying out every instant with alarm. Convulsive struggles continued after he was in bed, and he foamed at the mouth considerably. He was, however, perfectly sensible, and inquired, in hurried accents, what it could possibly be that induced such agony when in the water.—'Can it be saltpetre?' His anxious mother, in the greatest distress, now plainly perceived that hydrophobia was actually confirmed in her child; and made up her mind at once to understand that this her beloved one must be resigned into the arms of the almighty Jesus.

And now she felt how good it was that she could speak even to this young creature on the nature of the change that soon awaited him, with some confidence of being understood; for he had been early taught, and always loved the Bible,—listening with peculiar interest to the narratives recorded therein—and dwelling on her remarks and explanations of his parent on the various characters brought to his notice, with remarkable pleasure, and selecting particular passages and men as his favourites.

Presuming on the known state of the child's mind, she at once told him not to be alarmed, but that he was going to the Almighty! 'You are now going to heaven, my love'. He immediately caught the words; and, in the very midst of his convulsive efforts, interrogated quickly, 'To die? To the Almighty? To heaven?' As the spasms gradually lessened on the little sufferer, he repeatedly and very tenderly exclaimed, 'Mamma, don't cry! Papa, don't cry! I shall not go to hell—shall I?' He was assured to the contrary, and told that God for Christ's sake loved him, and would not suffer him to go to hell! 'You are going,' exclaimed the sorrowing father, 'my dear child, to Abraham's bosom, to Jesus Christ.' 'Yes,' replied this interesting young disciple, 'to Abraham's bosom—to Christ—to Elijah!'

The fits now recurred with considerable violence, yet he again entreated his parents not to weep, but to call on God's angels to come and take him. His mother urged him to pray—'I have prayed, my mamma—I do pray!' The convulsions became more powerful, and the respiration spasmodically quick and hurried, when he supplicated 'O Lord, have mercy. O Lord, Have mercy!' The voice was sweet and harmonious, and great emphasis and precision were given to the words 'Have mercy.' 'Oh papa, pray for me! dear mamma, pray for me'. Dreadful to witness were the struggles of the body; yet the soul seemed in perfect peace, and as if the body was enabled to bear its abounding sufferings by the abounding mercies of an indwelling Christ.

Again he exclaimed, 'O Elijah! O Lord! O my God!' His father assured him, 'You will soon be happy, and at rest, Johnny!' He replied, 'Oh yes, very happy!' Another awful struggle followed. The earthly shell seemed to cling fast hold of its imprisoned tenant, while the struggling soul seemed fighting to escape through the dark shadow of death, constantly ejaculating supplications for mercy.

United prayers were now offered up to the throne of grace and mercy, to take this young and beautiful plant—a flower of the Lord's own cherishing—to its kindred heaven; and our prayers were heard. The disease generally lasts eight days: here it only actually raged three hours. The fits seemed now less severe. As we were looking at and watching the little sufferer at the foot of the bed, he called out to me in a clear firm voice, 'Come here, sir, and shut my eyes! Aha! Aha!' said he, 'There! there! it is now over, papa, don't cry! mamma, don't cry!' He paused a moment—'Papa! mamma!' 'We

are close at your side, love!' He summoned me by name, also, to come near to him, and softly sighed out his soul into the hands of his Maker, with the affecting words, 'Mercy! Mercy! Happy! Happy!'

NEAR HOME OR, THE COUNTRIES OF EUROPE DESCRIBED

HOLLAND, OR THE NETHERLANDS

Now I am going to tell you of a country without any mountains—a country that is flat like a dish. Do you think it is a pretty country? Only one part is pretty, which is Guelderland. Holland is wet and unhealthy.

The people of Holland are called the Dutch. They are a very industrious people. They make their wet land as dry as they can by digging deep ditches and canals for the water to flow into. The canals are very useful. They are like roads from one place to another. Often may you see a boat in a canal, and a horse by the side drawing the boat and trotting along. This is a slow, but quiet way of travelling. There are canals in the streets. There are railways also now in all parts of the country.

The Dutch are very clean. They scrub the brass pans they use in their kitchens, till they shine like gold. If they did not rub them a great deal, the damp would perhaps spoil them. They are very fond of smoking. Some think it is the damp air which makes them delight so much in their pipes. They cannot talk while they are smoking; but they are not particularly fond of talking or laughing. They are a steady, quiet, grave people.

What sort of animals are there in Holland? There are goats and sheep. There are not many horses for riding; but there are strong horses to draw the boats slowly along; and there are

plenty of cows to eat the fine, fresh grass. There are also very obedient dogs, which draw little carts full of fish along the streets into the country.

The favourite bird is the stork. It is a tall bird with very long legs, a very long neck, a very long beak, and a small head. No wonder the Dutch love it, for it is so useful. With its long legs it can walk in the marshes, and with its long beak it can seize the croaking frogs, of which the marshes are full. When it walks in the streets, it eats the dead rats and mice, and so helps to keep the streets clean. The storks make no noise, yet they are playful creatures, and have been known to play at hide-and-seek with children.

There is no country in the world damper than Holland. There is so much water that every place is wet; indeed, people could not live there at all, if it were not for the pains they take to make it a little more dry. They dig little ditches close together all over the country, and let the water run into them. They also make great banks, to keep out the sea, and to prevent it from overflowing the land. These banks are called dykes. The cows are covered with sacking during the rainy season, lest they should get wet, and lest they should get fever by lying down in the very wet meadows.

You would be surprised to see how many

windmills there are in Holland. The use of the windmills is to pump water out of the wet ditches into the broad streams of water called canals. These are much prettier than the wet ditches. Willow-trees grow by the edge of the canals, and boats full of people float along. In winter some of these canals are covered with ice, and men and women, and children, may be seen skating to market, with their baskets on their heads.

The damp air makes the children's cheeks fresh and rosy. In Holland, people generally have light eyes and hair, and round faces.

They dress very much like English and French people. But some of the countrywomen wear gold plates on their heads and long golden earrings; and even poor girls will sometimes wear as much gold as would buy two cows in England.

There is no people in Europe who spend so much time cleaning their houses as the Dutch. It is pleasant to go into a Dutch kitchen. What a clean floor! The red bricks have just been rubbed over with fresh red sand. What bright copper kettles and saucepans! What a neat brick hearth! What pretty shining tiles on the walls!

The poor children at school are much cleaner than English children.

The Dutch are very industrious. The king will not allow big boys to stand idle in the streets. The policemen take up idle ragged boys, and send them into the country to drain the marshy grounds; so there are very few thieves, and hardly any beggars.

The Dutch children do not make so much noise at school as English children do. You hear no noise outside the school-house, and, when playtime comes, the scholars go out quietly. They cannot help making some noise with their feet, as they wear wooden shoes; and wooden shoes, I think, they must need to keep their feet dry in such a wet country.

Amsterdam is the old capital of Holland. There is no city in which there is so much danger of being drowned, for it is full of canals. The houses are all built on piles or posts, driven into the ground, and they are so well built that the people who live in them do not suffer from damp.

They are built in rows along the banks of the canals. Very often there are lines of trees between the houses and the canals. There are nearly three hundred bridges.

There are a great many rich people in Amsterdam, for Amsterdam is full of merchants; and their houses are solid and well built. Some of them are very old and curious. They are much larger than they appear. If you looked at the front windows of a house, you might think it was quite small, when it was not small at all. This is because the houses go so far back. They have marble passages, and some of the windows have very old glass, which was made in Venice, and which is tinted pink or violet. This glass is very valuable.

But though there is so much water in Amsterdam, there is very little water fit to drink, so that the people either buy water of men who bring water-carts, or they drink rain-water, which is kept in tanks. Still, the water of the canals is very useful for keeping the city clean. The servant-girls may be seen in the morning, in their wooden shoes, pouring buckets in the street, and dashing water against the sides of the houses.

GREECE

Look at the land at the bottom of Turkey. It is called Greece. It is a charming country; but who would like to live so near the Turks?

The Greeks have found it very unpleasant. Many of the Greeks have been obliged to hide themselves from the Turks among the rocks and mountains, and many of them have turned robbers. But now they have a king of their own, and they are no longer treated so ill as they used to be.

The Greeks have not the same religion as the Turks. They are called Christians, but they are not Protestants. Are they Roman Catholics? No, they do not mind the Pope of Rome. They are like the Russians, and their religion is called the Greek religion. In some things it is like the Roman Catholic religion. The Greeks bow down to pictures, though they do not worship images.

English people often go to Greece. And why? Is it to see the beautiful rivers and mountains that they go? Not only to see them, but for another reason. A great while ago there were in Greece marble palaces for kings, and temples for idols, and they are fallen down and lying upon the ground. People come from far to look at them. The great stones and broken pillars peep out among the long grass. There the goats browse and sport together. Who can be sorry that the idol temples are fallen down?

Does anything useful come from Greece? Yes, silk, for there are many mulberry-trees for the silk-worms. The sweetest honey comes from Greece, because there are so many sweet-smelling herbs there; such as thyme and rosemary; and bees suck the sweetest juices out of these plants.

Have you ever eaten plum-cake? But are those plums in the cake? No. Are they currants? No, they never grew on currant-bushes. They are grapes—very small grapes. Why, then, do we not say grape-cake instead of plum-cake? The reason is that these tiny grapes were called currants, because they were first brought from Corinth, which is a city of Greece.

March's 1d. Book of Sports.

THE ROCKING HORSE

If P'a goes to Epsom, I'll follow;
    The jockeys then quickly shall find
We can beat all the race horses hollow,
    And leave the steam coaches behind.

PLAYING AT SOLDIERS

Play up Tom Green, 'God save the Queen,'
    And 'Rule Britannia' too;
With colors gay we'll march away,
    And rival Waterloo!

THE WHEELBARROW RACE

Then quickly they place
For a blind-folded race,
Three wheelbarrows out on the green;
Where Ralph, Giles, and Pat
All start for a hat,
Such a gay one as seldom is seen!

But that wicked boy Miles
Whisper'd to Giles,
'Run more to the right and you'll win;'
Poor Giles took the way
That led him astray
To a large muddy ditch, and fell in.

THE WALK

The Day, how serene!
Not a whisper between
The leaves of the aspen or ash.
In this Midsummer heat
It will be a great treat
To loosen our favourite Dash.

Now hie boy! and take
A walk by the lake,
Where the air is so pleasant and cool;
But be sure that this cane
You bring back again,
When I cast it forth into the pool.

THE SAILING BOAT

How pleasant and cool
By the side of the pool
On a midsummer's even to stray,
And hear the bells ring,
Or nightingale sing
His sweet and melodious lay;

Or under the trees
In a beautiful breeze
To see my ship spread out her sail
In the sun's parting beam
As she ripples the stream,
And travels along with the gale.

THE SMOCK RACE

The folks all repair
To Nettlegreen Fair,
Where lads through a collar are grinning;
And Grace, Sue, and Jane
Bound over the plain,
The prize a fine new under linen.

Though I cannot tell why
A girl should be shy
Of owning a white linen smock;
Call the name what you please,
Shift, Shimmy, Chemise;
Or Miss Finikin's new body frock.

JUMPING IN SACKS

Rather slow is the pace
Of a Miller's sack race,
But it causes a rare bit of fun;
For some, if not all
Are so likely to fall
Before many yards have been run.

There's Mungo (the black)
Fix'd tight in his sack,
And has broken his nose on the ground;
While Zachary White,
He holds his up tight.
And jumps full three feet at a bound.

HOP SCOTCH

Now Helen and Jack,
If you only stand back
You'll see what a pitch I have got,
I am in number eight,
You'll now have to wait,
For I think I shall go on to pot.

That's all very fine,
But your toe's on the line;
Master Tom, I am not to be beat:
I see very clear
You do not play fair,
And I am sure it is wicked to cheat.

40

THE LUCKY PIG

At the close of the day
There was given away
A pig; but you'd got him to catch;
And that was not easy,
His tail was so greasy,
And at dodging he ne'er had his match.

Till trying at last
To hold Tiggy fast,
A wrangle produced a few blows;
While Toby ran by,
Got home to his sty,
Saved his bacon and cheated his foes.

THE CHAISE

The letter has come
Inviting me home,
Jane, get my clothes ready, I pray!
Like a princess I'll ride
With my P'a by my side
Come Jenny, don't be all the day,

For the letter,—it says,
He has bought me a chaise,
With a beautiful harness for Nat;
When I handle the reins,
From Windsor to Staines,
The folks will all ask, Who is that?

THE CHILDREN'S ANSWERS

Dumb Boy's Examination

A clergyman once paid a visit to a deaf and dumb asylum in London, for the express purpose of examining the children in the knowledge they possessed of Divine truth. A little boy, on this occasion, was asked in writing. 'Who made the world?'

He took up the chalk, and wrote underneath the question, 'In the beginning God created the heaven and the earth.'

The clergyman then inquired in a similar manner, 'Why did Jesus Christ come into the world?'

A smile of delight and gratitude rested on the countenance of the little fellow, as he wrote, 'This is a faithful saying, and worthy of all acceptation, that Christ Jesus came into the world to save sinners.'

A third question was then proposed, eminently adapted to call his most powerful feelings into exercise: 'Why were you born deaf and dumb while I can hear and speak?'

'Never,' said an eye-witness, 'shall I forget the look of holy resignation and chastened sorrow which sat on his countenance as he took up the chalk and wrote, "Even so, Father, for so it seemed good in thy sight."'

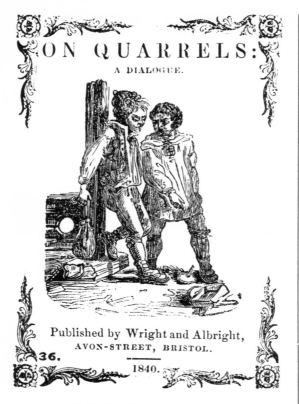

ON QUARRELS:
A DIALOGUE.

Published by Wright and Albright,
AVON-STREET, BRISTOL.

36.
———
1840.

ON QUARRELS: A DIALOGUE

'OH, WILLIAM, (said Frank to his eldest brother,) I have been wanting to see you ever since school was done. Just look at my head, and see where Robert struck me.

William. Robert struck you?

Frank. Yes, and only because I wouldn't change my large marble for three of his small ones.

W. Are you sure that was all? Perhaps you were a little provoking to him. Think a moment; and if you were in fault, say so honestly.

F. No, I am sure I was not in fault. James saw us both, and he can tell you so.

W. That is well. But did you strike him again?

F. Oh no. If I had, my head would have been swelled worse than this, I can tell you. Why, he is half as big again as I am. But I told him you would give him a good flogging.

W. Indeed! Then I have more concern in the matter than I thought at first. When would you like to have me do it?

F. The sooner the better. I guess we can catch him some time this afternoon.

W. Very well. I am willing to do any thing in reason to oblige you. But is it not strange, that two such particular friends as you and Robert should be trying to get each other flogged?

F. Oh, we are not friends now, by a great deal. We used to be rather intimate; but he was so cross and bad-tempered, that we could not agree together, and lately we have been a good deal more like enemies than friends.

W. Enemies? Oh that alters the case entirely. If that is the reason you want him flogged, I cannot give you any assistance in the matter.

F. Why not? I don't see how there could be any stronger reason.

W. As to that, we must try to find a good reason as well as a strong one. You know I try to act according to the principles of the Bible. Now, among all the instructions that Christ and the Apostles gave, there is nothing plainer or clearer than that we must never hurt our enemies, nor try to punish them for what they have done to us. Didn't you know that, Frank?

F. Yes, I remember what is said about loving our enemies; but does that mean such sort of enemies as Robert and I?

W. I suppose it means enemies of every sort; but you shall judge for yourself. Do you know where we can find a Testament?

F. Oh yes, there are plenty in the house. ...

W. Our duty is to feel and show such a spirit as [Christ's]; but the particular way in which we are to show it, is left to our own choice. Thus it might be proper, when Robert struck you, either to turn the other cheek literally, or to walk away quietly and leave him, or mildly to remonstrate with him as Christ did... But it could not possibly mean that you should strike him again, or try to get him flogged for it. Do you see this clearly, Frank?

F. Yes, I believe so. But mustn't I do anything to Robert, after his striking me so?

W. Oh yes; if the matter should be left here, perhaps he would strike you again. We must do something to make him remember it, and repent of it.

F. Yes, that is just what I thought. Now what would be the best way to do it.

W. One very good way would be to go to him pleasantly this afternoon, and offer to exchange marbles, as he wanted to before.

F. What, give him my marble after he struck me?

W. Why yes! If the object is to make him sorry that he struck you, and ashamed ever to do so again, I can't think of any better way to do it.

F. It seems a very strange way to me. If I give

up to him now, he will think I am afraid of him, and then he will get away every thing of mine he wants.

W. You are mistaken, Frank. Robert is a sensible and well-disposed boy; but he is a little passionate, and sometimes does things in his anger that he is sorry for afterwards. I dare say he he is sorry now that he struck you, and if you show a forgiving disposition, and act kindly and pleasantly towards him, he will be very careful not to do so again. I should not wonder if you became better friends than ever. What do you think of that Frank?

F. I don't know but we shall; for I don't feel half so cross about it as I did.

THE HINDOO GIRL SEEKING JESUS

A Hindoo girl was playing before the door of her father's house. Some wicked men came that way and, taking her in their arms, ran away with her to a distant place, where they sold her as a slave.

An Indian lady, who bought the girl, soon loved her as her own child. She had her dressed in fine clothes and many jewels. Everything was done to make her happy, and to lead her to forget the home of her early days.

Time passed away. As the girl grew in years, she felt that she was a sinner. She did not know what made her so feel. All she knew was, that she was a sinner, and could not tell how sin was to be forgiven.

When she spoke to the lady about it, she got no comfort, for the lady had never heard of the only way in which a sinner can find peace.

'Oh,' she cried, 'I shall die in my sins.'

One day she was sitting full of sorrow, when a Hindoo beggar came to the door. He told her that he had come from a place where many of the people were called Christians, for they believed in a holy one, named Jesus Christ, who could save from sin.

'Oh, show me the way to this place and to these people,' she said.

'Why, that I will do,' replied the man. 'If you go to a village some miles away, you will find a Hindoo, who has become one of these Christians. He was once a rich native, but he has given up all his worldly goods that he may follow Christ. He will tell you what you should do.'

A few days after this time, the Hindoo girl was on her way to the village; and as she went along, she asked those she met if they could tell her where the man lived who led the people to Jesus. Some mocked, and others scolded, saying she should not forsake the gods of her country.

At last she thought she must give up the search. She was in a strange part of the country, and was tired and worn out with her journey. When, just then she met a Hindoo, and once more she asked, 'Can you tell me the way to the man who knows Jesus Christ?' To her great joy, she found that he knew what she meant, and he pointed out the road to the teacher's house.

When she came to the door, as soon as she saw the teacher, she cried, 'I want you to take me to Jesus, who takes away sin. Oh, take me to him *now;* I want him to remove sin from my heart.'

The Christian native heard her tell of her sorrow, and how she had gone about in search of peace without finding it.

The pious teacher than spoke to her of the Son of God, who was once on earth, and who invited sinners to come to him that they might be saved.

As the Hindoo maiden heard these good words, hope came into her mind. She saw that Jesus was the only Saviour, and in him she could find rest for her soul.

After staying some days at the mission-house, she returned home.

We can tell no more about this young Hindoo. If she yet lives, we hope she knows more of Jesus, and loves him better than when she first went forth to seek him.

This true story is given to show that there is no peace to be found until a sinner believes in Jesus Christ.

TALES ABOUT RAILWAYS

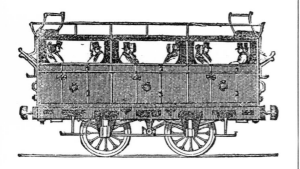

WHAT a change—what a wonderful change from the slow movements of the days of our fathers, has this new mode of motion made. Some old people dont know what to make of it. A few years ago, I visited the village of my ancestors, a small secluded spot in a remote corner of a midland county. It was about seven o'clock one fine morning in autumn, when I jumped off the coach at the 'guide post' which stands among the yet unenclosed fields which my relatives have reaped for generations, and walking down them, I entered the old farm house, and there I found my aged aunt busy with her butter and cheese, just as she was wont to be more than forty years ago, when I, a little merry lad, had come to 'uncle's' for a holiday.

After taking a cup of coffee, we sat down and talked.

'Come and see us, aunt. You can come now. Cousin can drive you to N——, and then you will be with us in two hours by rails.'

'Oh, no! I cannot leave home now. I am too old. Besides, I dont like these railways. People get killed by them, they say.'

'Not so many as were by coaches, aunt. They are more safe, I think, upon the whole, and much more easy. Why, aunt, they tell me you are to have a line come close by here.'

Turning my head and looking down the lane, I exclaimed—

'Why, here they are, the very men.'

'Who ?'

'Why, the men who make the railways. Do you see that carriage with two white horses, and the men with red flag staffs! and those sharp looking gentlemen who are jumping out of the carriage—they are the engineers. Why, they are coming up here. They are bold fellows, these men: they go over people's lands without asking anybody's leave. And if your house, or barn, or stables, stand in their way, they will knock them all down to make a railroad.'

And up they did come, and walked very deliberately over the homestead and orchard, and then went into some adjoining fields, and having made their observations and noted them down, they went back to their carriage, and drove off without saying a word to anybody. My dear old aunt was alarmed: but they avoided the village altogether, and went at a short distance from it. Some of the lands of my relative, however, were required for the intended line.

There is one thing about these railways which often causes some amusement, and that is their time of starting. People must be there in time, or they will be left behind. Many, however, have thought that they might take five minutes as they used to do with coaches; but when they got there, the train was, perhaps, two miles on its way! If this system should teach such people a good lesson or two on punctuality, it may do them good.

Some time ago I had a lesson. I was invited to a tea festival at a village about fifteen miles off, eleven of which were by rails, and then a friend was to meet me with a conveyance. A friend of mine, a minister in the neighbourhood, calling in, agreed to accompany me. We left my house in good time, secured our tickets, and walked quite leisurely on to the platform, but not seeing that the train was about to start, we did not perceive it till the whistle made us look sharp about us, and then only to discover, to our mortification, that our train was moving, and as it was no use calling 'Stop the coach,' we were left behind.

I thought a good deal about that door being shut: and I then thought of those words of our Lord, 'and the door was shut.' Will my young readers think of that too? It is a sad thing for any person who is going a long journey on important business to be 'too late', and find the door shut and the train gone. But far more sad and serious will be the condition of those who neglect to enter the way of life, the door of which now stands open, but which once shut, will be shut for ever.

Remember, Jesus Christ is the way to eternal life. Trust yourself to him, and you will be safe.

MAJA'S ALPHABET

A
a

A is Ann, with milk from the cow.

B
b

B is Benjamin, making a bow.

C
c

C is Charlotte, gathering flowers.

D
d

D is Dick, who is one of the mowers.

E
e

E is Eliza, feeding a hen.

F
f

F is Frank, who is mending his pen.

G g

G is Georgiana, shooting an arrow.

H h

H is Harry, wheeling a barrow.

I i

I is Isabella, gathering fruit.

J j

J is John, who is playing the flute.

K k

K is Kate, nursing her dolly.

L l

L is Lawrence, feeding poor Polly.

M m

M is Maja, learning to draw.

N n

N is Nicholas, with a jackdaw.

O o

O is Octavius, riding a goat.

P p

P is Penelope, sailing a boat.

Q q

Q is Quintus, armed with a lance.

R r

R is Rachel, learning to dance.

S s

S is Sarah, talking to cook.

T t

T is Teddy, reading a book.

U u

U is Urban, rolling the green.

V v

V is Victoria. Long live the Queen.

W is Walter, flying a kite.

Y is Miss Youthful, eating her bread,

X is Xerxes, a boy of great might.

and Z is Zachariah, going to bed.

THE HAPPY COTTAGERS

THE BREAKFAST

A poor but gracious man returning to his home from his early morning labour, at the usually allowed half hour to breakfast, found his wife, an indolent unthinking woman, still in bed, and no provision made for him. He cried out, 'What! not up yet, Mary?'—'No,' says she, 'Thomas I was very poorly, and could not arise.'—'Very well, child,' the poor man answered, 'Lie still, I will get the breakfast.' So, looking round for the tinder-box to strike a light, and then for the pitcher to get some water, the poor man bustled about. Finding however, no water in the pitcher he hastened to the well: and when at length the water boiled, the next object was to find some tea. 'There is none,' cries Mary, 'but only a few tea-leaves in the bason, given me yesterday by Mrs—.'

With great satisfaction Thomas warmed the leaves in the water, and cutting a slice of bread from the loaf standing on the shelf: having all things now spread upon the table, with uplifted eyes he thus bespoke his sense of the divine goodness. 'Blessed be God, (says Thomas), thou art a faithful God, true to thy word and to thy promises.—Thou hast said, *Bread shall be given, and water shall be sure;* and here they are this day, blessed be God in Jesus Christ.'—How sweet a proof of the evidence of grace in the heart! What but this could have wrought so heavenly an effect.

THE DINNER

There was a poor woman remarkable in the neighbourhood where she lived for the great cheerfulness always manifested in her behaviour. Whether things were well or ill, Martha seemed to be always happy. Some ladies of the village where she lived, calling upon Martha, at her lit-

48

tle hut in their morning walk, found the poor woman in the act of praising God for her dinner. 'And what have you had for dinner, Martha?' says one of the ladies to her. 'Madam,' says Martha, 'this is the remains,' showing them a crust of barley bread. 'Well, but Martha,' replied the lady, 'what have you had beside?' 'Nothing Madam,' answered the poor woman, looking as she said it, pleased and happy. 'It is poor fare, indeed, Martha,' replied the lady, 'and I wish you had better.' 'Blessed be the Lord,' said Martha, 'for this; I never desire better. I have enjoyed Christ with my crust, and the crust with my Christ; and is not this rich living?'

THE SUPPER

The evening happened to close with more than usual darkness, when a gentleman, who had extended his walk beyond the path of the turnpike road, found himself at a loss to discover the right way. A little light issuing from a small taper in the window of a cottage near him, induced the gentleman to make towards it, in hopes to gain information of the shortest way to the town. As he approached the door, he heard a voice in prayer; and standing to listen, he discovered that it was the father of the family, with his household at their evening devotions.

He waited until the poor man finished, and then without ceremony, opened the door and went in. The gentleman took occasion to notice the happiness of his mind, from the expression he had observed in the poor man's prayers. 'Sir', replied he, 'no one can have more reason for thankfulness to the Lord than I. We have every thing that the heart can wish, and it is but right that all our blessings should be prayed over, and God be thanked for them.'—'What have you no troubles?' says the gentleman. 'Oh yes, Sir!' cried the poor man, 'we are not without our troubles more than our neighbours. But then, by praying over them the Lord blesses *them* also. And when I see that the Lord appoints them, I am sure they will turn to good.' ...

While this conversation was passing between the poor man and his visitor, the supper was serving up for the family. 'You are come, Sir,' said the Cottager, 'in a happy season if you will have the goodness to partake. It is not always that we have a hot supper!' 'And what is it, my friend,' repplied the gentleman, 'that you have for supper?' 'A herby-pie, Sir,' said the host, 'and a good one I believe it is. Do, Sir, sit down, you are kindly welcome.' The gentleman was astonished at what he saw and heard. Alas! what mistaken calculations of real happiness do the great ones of the earth make!

THE SWEARER'S PRAYER, & C

WHAT, a swearer pray? Yes, swearer; whether thou thinkest so or not, each of thine oaths is a prayer,—an appeal to the holy and almighty God, whose name thou darest so impiously to take into thy lips.

And what is it, thinkest thou, swearer, that thou dost call for, when the awful imprecations, damn, and damnation, roll so frequently from thy profane tongue? Tremble, swearer, while I tell thee! Thy prayer contains two parts: thou prayest, First, that thou mayest be deprived of eternal happiness! Second, that thou mayest be plunged into eternal misery!

When therefore, thou callest for damnation, dost thou not, in effect, say as follows? 'O God! thou hast power to punish me in hell for ever: therefore, let not one of my sins be forgiven! Let every oath that I have sworn, every lie that I

have told, every Sabbath that I have broken, and all the sins that I have committed, either in thought, word, or deed, rise up in judgement against me, and eternally condemn me! Let me never partake of thy salvation! May my soul and body be deprived of all happiness, both in this world and that which is to come. Let me never see thy face with comfort; never enjoy thy favour and friendship; and let me never enter into the kingdom of heaven!'

This is the first part of thy prayer. Let us hear the second.

'O God, let me not only be shut out of heaven, but also let me be shut up in hell! May all the members of my body be tortured with inconceivable agony, and all the powers of my soul tormented with horror and despair, inexpressible and eternal! Let my dwelling be in the blackness of darkness, and my companions accursed men, and accursed devils! Pour down thy hottest anger; execute all thy wrath and curse upon me; arm and send forth all thy terrors against me; and let thy fierce, thy fiery, thy fearful indignation rest upon me! Be mine eternal enemy, and plague and punish and torment me in hell, for ever, and ever, and ever!!!'

Swearer, this is thy prayer!!! Oh dreadful imprecation! Oh horrible! horrible!! most horrible!!! Blaspheming man! dost thou like thy petition? Look at it. Art thou sincere in thy prayer, or art thou mocking thy Maker? Dost thou wish for damnation? Art thou desirous of eternal torment? If so, swear on—swear hard! The more oaths, the more misery; and, perhaps, the sooner thou mayest be in hell! Art thou shocked at this language? Does it harrow up thy soul? Does thy very blood run cold in thy veins? Art thou convinced of the evil of profane swearing? How many times hast thou blasphemed the God of heaven? How many times hast thou asked God to damn thee, in the course of a year, a month, a day? Nay, how many times in a single hour hast thou called for damnation? Art thou not yet in hell? Wonder, O heavens, and be astonished. O earth, at the goodness and long-suffering of that God whose great name swearing persons so often and so awfully profane! Swearer, be thankful, oh, be exceedingly thankful, that God has not answered thy prayer! thy tremendous prayer! that his mercy and patience have withholden the request of thy polluted lips! Never let him hear another oath from thy unhallowed tongue, lest it should be thy last expression upon earth, and thy swearing prayer should be answered in hell. Oh, let thine oaths be turned into supplications! Repent, and turn to Jesus, who died for swearers, as well as for his murderers. And then, oh! then, (though thou mayest have sworn as many oaths as there are 'stars in the heavens, and sands upon the sea-shore innumerable,') then thou shalt find, to thy eternal joy, that there is love enough in his heart, and merit sufficient in his blood, to pardon thy sins, and save thy soul for ever. Swearer! canst thou ever again blaspheme such a God and Saviour as this? Does not thy conscience cry, God forbid? Even so. Amen.

In November, 1786, a person much given to swearing, being disappointed by one of his companions not returning to the public house as soon as he expected, swore he would never drink with him again, and that if he did, it should be his last. Accordingly that day was his last. God took him at his word, and thus called him into eternity.

In November, 1787, one W——rs, a smith, spending the evening at a public house, in Leather-lane, quarrelled with one of his companions, and, while swearing one of the most horrid oaths, God struck him instantaneously dead, with an oath on his lips, upon the bench where he was sitting. The jury who sat upon the body, after hearing all the circumstances of the case, brought in their verdict—That W——rs was struck dead as a judgment from God. This narration was given by the foreman of the jury.

Another remarkable judgment overtook a person living in Brewer-street, Soho, who, cursing and swearing in a most dreadful manner, was struck speechless, and died the same afternoon.

T.G. who lived in the parish of Sedgley, near Wolverhampton, having lost a considerable sum at cock-fighting, to which practice he was notoriously addicted, swore in a most horrid manner that he would never fight another cock, frequently calling upon God to damn his soul to all eternity if he did; and, with dreadful imprecations, wishing the devil might fetch him, if ever he made another bet. His resolution, thus impiously formed, was, for a while, observed; but, about two years afterwards, Satan, whose willing servant he continued to be, inspired him with a violent desire to attend a cocking at Wolverhampton; and he complied with the temptation. He there stood up, and cried, 'I hold four to three on such a cock.' 'Four what?' said one of his companions in iniquity. 'Four shillings,' replied he. Upon which the wager was confirmed, and he, putting his hand into his pocket for the money, instantly fell a ghastly corpse upon the ground.

'Who hath hardened himself against God, and prospered?' Job ix.4.

'Thou shalt not take the name of the Lord thy God in vain, for the Lord will not hold him guiltless that taketh his name in vain.' Exod. xx.7.

'Because of swearing, the land mourneth.' Jer.xxii.10.

'Every one that sweareth shall be cut off.' Zech.v.3.

Dear reader, art thou a swearer? Oh, take this friendly warning. The next oath may be the last: if thy prayer is heard, thy soul is damned for ever!!!

WONDERS
OF
A TOY - SHOP.

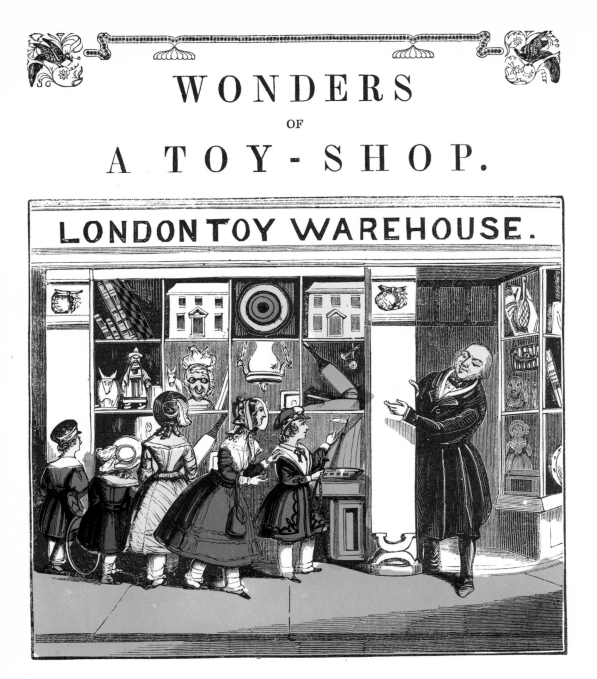

LONDON TOY WAREHOUSE.

" Pray, what would you like?" said a Toyman,
    one day,
      Addressing a group of young folks;
" I have toys in abundance, and very cheap, too,
      Though not quite so cheap as my jokes.

"Here's a wagon well laden, and here is a dray,
   With horses and harness complete;
You can drive them in parlour and drawing-
      room, too,
   As easily as through the street.

"Here's a whole file of soldiers quite ready for
      fight,
   And each of them armed with a gun;
You may knock them all down with a feather,
      and then
   You may pocket them—every one.

"A doll's pretty kitchen, stands next on the shelf,
With grate, pans, and kettle, and pot;
With dish and tureen, and all crockery-ware,
Knives and forks, and I cannot tell what:

"They would not quite do for a great city feast,
But, I think I may venture to say,
A minnow or tittlebat there might be cooked,
As a rarity on Lord Mayor's day,

" A full set of bricks is enclosed in this box,
    (With the mortar we well may dispense,)
But with these you may build a magnificent
        house,
    Without e'en a farthing's expense:

"With these you may raise up a Royal Exchange,
    In less than five minutes;—and then
Knock it down, and build up a new Parliament
        House,
    In another five minutes,—or ten.

POOR JACK, THE SAILOR BOY

SOME MONTHS since, at a Bible meeting, a person very decently dressed in black, came forward on the platform; and after a very powerful appeal to the audience in favour of Bible Societies, he remarked, that a little boy in a seaport town, some years since, had a most passionate and reprobate father, who was a sailor. One evening, the lad was sent to the pier to call his father, and finding him in a state of intoxication some conversation ensued. The father, enraged at a remark from the boy, raised his foot, and kicked him from the edge of the pier into the sea. In a storm of passion the father reeled to the public-house. The night was approaching fast, the poor child was struggling with the waves, and nearly sinking, when a sloop-of-war's boat going off to the ship espied him, and providentially saved him from a watery grave. The ship was under sailing orders, and weighed that night. Every attention was paid by the seamen to the lad, and next day, on hearing his simple but affecting tale, they christened him, 'Poor Jack.'

The ship was going on a foreign station. Jack soon became an active useful boy; his natural good temper and smartness in duty, procured him many friends, and in a few years Jack was a favourite with all on board. Happily, in this ship, God had not left himself without a witness; one or two men were not ashamed to read their Bibles, and publicly owned their attachment to a crucified Saviour. Poor Jack was kindly noticed by them, and mercifully awakened by divine grace.

Several men had died, and fresh drafts had often been received on board. Jack's history was almost forgotten. An action was fought, and several men killed and wounded. The latter, after being properly arranged in the sick bay, were often humanely visited by Jack. An old sailor, in particular, who was badly wounded, and not expected to live, received much Christian care from him. In finding the current of life fast ebbing away, he became deeply concerned for his precious and immortal soul, and was often found bathed in tears on account of his sins. On these occasions Jack failed not to read the sacred Scriptures, and point out such portions as were most applicable to a sinner convinced of his guilt and danger, and anxious to flee from the wrath to come. The poor, old sailor at length perceived a ray of hope, and was encouraged to take refuge in Him who died for the chief of sinners. A cloud of horror, nevertheless, so overwhelmed him, that he could not firmly lay hold of the hope set before him, though he dared not altogether reject it. A few days before he died, Jack was standing by his hammock, when a sudden gush of tears, and a death-like howl, burst from the old man, and he faintly uttered, 'O, I cannot be pardoned! No, no! I am, young man, I am a murderer! O, my child, my child! my boy, my dear boy! There, see how he struggles with the waves! hark! he cries for help! yes, I heard him say, "Father, save me!"—O, save him! Throw a rope over; launch the boat out! Will no one save him! Ah! he sinks, and his father is his murderer! Yes, reproach me, Mary! Shriek again, again, as wild as before, and cry, "Give me my child! where is my boy!" Poor Mary, thou art cold in death! I can't get drunk now, and forget thy sorrows. I am wounded! I am dying! Vengeance has overtaken me! O, the terrors of a guilty conscience.'

Overwhelmed with pity, love, joy, and wonder, Poor Jack, in an agony of tears, fell on the neck of the old sailor, crying, 'My father, my father, my father! behold your son, your boy! I did not perish; the ship's boat saved me. O, there is mercy for you, my father, my father!'

'What,' cried the trembling and astonished old man, 'are you my boy, my own child, the lad I dashed from the pier?'

'Yes, my father, believe me, I am, I am. Ever since you have been wounded, I have felt the most unaccountable attraction towards you; day by day my bowels have yearned over you. I loved you more than any man I ever saw. I counted myself most happy to read and pray with you. I often wondered at my feeling; the mystery is now explained. I have been attending my father; I have been comforting my father!'

'My child: yes, thou art my child! I see the features of my dear Mary!' A mutual flood of tears prevented either speaking for some minutes. At length the youth exclaimed, 'Merciful God, how wondrous are thy ways! O save, save,

I beseech a father, whom thou hast graciously spared, and with whom thou hast so unexpectedly brought me acquainted.'

Jack paused; the father rejoiced; joy and gratitude beamed in his countenance. Heaven smiled on the dying man; and a still, small voice communicated to his soul a peace which passeth all understanding. But the scene grows too painful to be prolonged; suffice it to say, poor Jack's father lived several days after this, and died rejoicing in God, the Saviour of his soul. A year or two passed over and the war ended. The ship was paid off, and Jack, being cast on shore, employed his time and talents in urging sinners to flee for refuge to Jesus Christ.

The speaker paused—with much modesty and humility, he exclaimed, 'Ladies and Gentlemen, in the relater of this anecdote you now see Poor Jack.'

———————•———————

THE NEW BRIGHT PENNY

LITTLE HARRY's father was a poor man, and it was rarely that a penny found its way into Harry's pocket, except on a sabbath, when his father would give each of his children a penny to put into the mission box.

One sabbath, as Harry was about starting off for sabbath school, his father called to him and said, 'Here, Harry, is a penny for you to put into the mission box.' It was a new bright penny, and it looked very nice to Harry as he took it into his hand; and the thought came into his head 'I wish it was mine to keep.' Now, what was Harry to do when this bad thought came into

his mind? Why, he should have driven it right out again, and asked God to help him to do what was right.

As Harry went on to the sabbath school, he kept taking the bright penny out of his pocket, and looking at it; and every time he wished more and more that he could keep it. While he was in the school, he thought about the penny in his pocket, and kept counting how many marbles he could buy. Harry then made up his mind to keep the penny, but his heart told him that he was doing wrong.

Harry went home with the rest, but he was not happy all day: that penny in his pocket seemed to press like lead on his heart; he felt it all the time; he did not think a penny could feel so heavy. When his mother and brothers and sisters sang sweet hymns, he could not join them, for there was a lump in his throat which felt as if the penny itself was sticking there. In the evening their mother began to question them as usual, and when she made this remark, that a single sin would call down the anger of God upon us, Harry left his seat and came round and stood by his mother, and laid his hand on her shoulder. As she went on talking, she heard a sob, and looking round, she saw that Harry was crying as if his heart would break. 'What is the matter, Harry?' she asked; but Harry only kneeled down on the floor, and laid his head on his mother's knee, and cried.

When the time came for them to go to bed, Harry went up with the rest. His brothers were soon asleep, but Harry tossed about on his pillow, and could not sleep or rest; the lump in his throat seemed as if it would choke him; a great many times he was on the point of calling to his mother, and telling her. After a time, he heard his father and mother locking the doors. 'Now', said he, 'they are going to bed, and if I do not tell mother now, I shall not sleep any to-night.' So he sat up in his bed, and in a husky voice called, 'Mother, will you come up here one moment, mother?' His mother came; he asked her for a drink of water; she gave it to him, and said, 'Is that all you want, Harry?' 'No, mother,' said Harry; 'I cannot sleep till I tell you what a wicked thing I did today:' he then told his mother all about it. She sat down beside him, and talked to him for a long time, and then told him to get up and kneel down by her, and confess his sin to God; 'for though God knows it all,' said she, 'he tells us to confess our sins to him.' Harry knelt by his mother, and in broken words with many tears, did he confess his sin. After he had lain down in bed again, he said, 'Tell me this, mother; will you always be afraid to trust me after this?' 'No, my boy, I shall not be afraid to trust you, for I think you have had a lesson to day which you will never forget; but you must not forget to pray daily that God will keep you from evil. Good night, my boy;' and his mother kissed him, and went away. In a few minutes she came back, and looked at Harry; he was lying with the cheek resting on his hand; the tears were yet on his eye-lashes, but the troubled look had passed away from his face, and he was in a sweet and happy sleep.

PETER PARLEY

INQUISITIVE JACK AND HIS AUNT MARY

INTRODUCTION

Although I profess to deal in matters that may amuse my young friends, I have a constant desire that, while they are entertained, they shall be instructed. The only way to be happy—really and truly happy—is to be wise; and wisdom comes through teaching.

You know there are such people as savages—who roam wild in the woods, or dwell in wigwams, sitting upon the ground, and sleeping upon the skins of beasts; who have no books, nor schools, nor churches; who have never read the Bible; who know nothing of Jesus Christ, nor of the ten commandments.

Well, what makes the difference between these wild, savage people, and those who live in good houses, in towns and cities, and have all the comforts and conveniences of life? Knowledge makes the whole difference, and knowledge comes by education. Do my little readers know that without education they would be savages? Yet it is really so. All are born alike—the child of the savage, and the child of the Christian: one grows up a savage, because its father and mother do not send it to school, do not furnish it with books, do not teach it to read and write; the other grows up a Christian, because it is educated. Education, therefore, makes us to differ.

Our good Father in heaven, whom we all ought to love and obey, did not intend us to be savages; but he has provided only one way to avoid it, and that is by education. He makes it our duty, therefore, as well as our happiness, to seek for instruction.

This design of our Creator is very apparent when we compare man with animals. Birds and beasts do not go to school; they are provided with all needful knowledge by that power which we call instinct. A little chicken, only a day old, will run about and pick up seeds, which lie scattered among the stones and dirt. How does the chicken know that seeds are made to eat, and that stones are not made to eat? How does the chicken distinguish the wholesome and nutritious seed from the dirt and gravel? God has taught it— God has given it a wonderful instinct, by which it is guided in the choice and discovery of its food.

But the infant has no such instinct; left to itself, it will pick up dirt, stones, pins— anything that comes in its way— and put all into its little mouth! The child has to be taught everything by its parents or its nurse. It must be taught what is good and what is evil—what to seek, and what to shun.

The chicken runs about as soon as it is hatched; the child must be taught first to creep, then to walk. The chicken, left to itself, though but a day old, will hide from the hawk that would devour it; the child, if left to itself, wolud as soon go into the fire, the water, or the bear's mouth, as anywhere else. The chicken is guided by instinct—the child by instruction.

Thus it appears that, while instinct is the guide of the animal world, education is the instrument by which children are to reach their true destiny. God meant us to be educated; and children who hate education, hate God's will and God's way; they hate the road that leads to their own happiness. Think of that—think that when you resist instruction, you resist the will of Providence, and sin against your own peace!

CHAPTER I.
JACK'S MODE OF SATISFYING HIS CURIOSITY
THE ANT-HILL

One day in spring Jack was in the garden. By and by he happened to see an ant running along with a piece of leaf in his mouth. The little insect paddled along with his six legs very fast, and soon came to a little hillock of earth, about as large as a wash-hand basin turned upside down.

It seemed to consist of a heap of particles of sand. Now Jack, instead of running away to tell his mother about what he had seen, remained to *observe* and look into the matter, or *investigate* it. On looking at the little mound, he saw there were a number of holes in it; and into one of them the little ant with the leaf, plunged head first. 'I wonder where he is gone to?' said Jack. In a minute or two several ants came out of these holes, and some of them had small white things that looked like eggs. These they laid down in the sun, and went into their holes to fetch more.

Every ant seemed to be busy about something. Jack saw several ants go away from the hill. He determined to observe them, and find out what was going on. He watched one fellow particularly, and he went to the distance of as much as three yards. There was a large dead fly. The ant went to work, gnawed off his head, took it in his teeth, and scrambled back to the hill, and down he went into one of the holes.

In a few seconds he came back, made another journey to the dead fly, sawed off another portion, and transported it to the hill. In this way he kept going out and in, and in the course of an hour, the ant had carried off the whole carcase. 'Well,' said Jack to himself, 'I suppose that fellow is the butcher, and supplies the ant-folks with meat!'

While all this was going on, Jack had time to observe and investigate other things. He saw one ant go as much as a dozen times to a dandelion, and load himself with the yellow powder which he gathered from the blossoms. 'I suppose this must be the baker!' said Jack. He saw several climb up the stalks of tall plants, to get the juice or honey from ten blossoms. 'These fellows seem to be the grocers!' said the boy.

By and by, Jack saw an ant going along, when he chanced to arrive at another hill. Immediately he began to smell about this way and that — but an ant upon the strange hill saw him. In he went, at a hole, and in a few seconds he sallied forth with five or six others in his rear. They darted forward, heels over head, towards the intruder, the strange ant. He had become aware of the danger, and was galloping back towards his own hill as fast as his legs could carry him. Jack looked on with as much interest as if it had been a fox-chase.

The little red ant that had stirred up this affray went straight ahead, and pretty soon came to a ball of earth as big as a walnut. Deeming it better to climb over than to go round it, he began to mount, when the leader among the pursuers, a large black ant, stuck his teeth into him. The red ant turned round and grappled; both fell backwards, and rolled upon the earth, when there followed a great deal of scratching and biting.

At last little Red escaped—having given Black a severe wound. The others now came up, and the chase was resumed. By and by the party approached Red's home. Here he met some of his friends. They carried the alarm to the hill. In a few seconds, at least fifty ants, all red, sallied forth. 'I imagine these are the soldiers!' says Jack—and so they were, sure enough.

It was claw to claw—teeth to teeth. They pulled and hauled—bit and scratched; and after a few minutes, the battle was over. One large black ant was killed. He was cut into four pieces, and the Reds carried him home, no doubt for a feast.

While Jack was busy in observing and investigating these things, he heard his mother's call.

Though he had been engaged at least four hours in observing these things, he was not weary, and would gladly have staid longer; but being an obedient and good boy, he forthwith went to his mother, and found his dinner ready. It was one advantage of his morning exercise, that the fresh air had given him a good appetite.

CHAPTER II.
THE STORY OF THE DEAD HORSE-FLY

As he had now learned something about the ants, he desired to know more; so he used very often to go and look at them. He did not stamp with his heel on the ant-hills, and crush the houses of the little busy creatures. Some boys do this, and think there is fun in it; but Jack looked upon all innocent and harmless creatures with a feeling of affection, and he loved rather to help them, than to kill or disturb them.

One day he found a large dead horse-fly; so he took it and laid it down at a little distance from the ant-hill, and soon saw one of the ants come near the fly. He took hold of it and tried to carry it; then pulled and hauled it with all his might; but finding that he could not manage it, he set off for the hill. He there met several of his companions. He went close to them, and seemed to touch them with his little feelers. Immediately four of them set off with him, and went to the dead fly.

When they got to the dead fly, they took hold of it, and began to drag it towards the hill. It was twice as big as all the five ants put together; but they jerked, and pulled, and twitched, and it was really quite wonderful to see how fast they got the carcase over the rough earth. Every ant did his best; there was no lazy fellow among them, skulking and shamming so as to put off the hard work upon his companions.

In a very short time, the ants had brought the fly to the hill; immediately they began to cut up the fly, for he was too big to be got into one of their houses. One sawed off a leg, another a wing, and another the head; each carrying his piece into the hill. In the space of about five minutes the fly was cut to pieces, and stowed away in the city of the ants.

Jack was greatly delighted with what he saw. Every evening he used to tell his father and mother what he had observed during the day, and they were always pleased with his simple stories.

CHAPTER XIX.
ABOUT POETRY

One winter's day, as he and his aunt were sitting by a pleasant fire, Jack had been reading in a book of poetry. After a while, he laid down the book, and asked his aunt why some things are told in poetry and some in prose. To this the good lady replied as follows:

I must tell you in the first place, my boy, that prose is the language of common speech, such as I am now talking to you. But there are certain thoughts and feelings that are too fine and beautiful for prose. If these were expressed in a common way their beauty would be lost. I will try to make you understand this by a story.

'There were once some flowers growing in a garden, but they were mixed with other plants, such as peas, beans, potatoes, beets, and other things. These had, therefore, a common appearance, and no one noticed their beauty. At length the gardener took up these flowers, and set them out in a nice bed of earth which he had prepared for them. This situation permitted their bright colours and fair forms to be seen, and they therefore attracted the attention of every person who passed by.

'Everybody admired them, and those who overlooked them as common things when

planted in a kitchen garden were ready to acknowledge their beauty and praise their fragrance, when they were flourishing in a flower garden. Thus, you perceive, that I compare fine thoughts to flowers; however beautiful they may be, they would strike us less and please us less if they were presented in a common way. They want a situation appropriate to them, and then we shall perceive and feel their full beauty.

'Poetry, then, consists of beautiful thoughts in beautiful language, and may be compared to a bed of flowers, with graceful forms, bright colours, and sweet fragrance. Prose consists of common thoughts expressed in common language, and may be compared to a garden filled with things that are useful rather than beautiful, such as beets, potatoes, and cabbages.'

Jack listened with great attention to what his aunt had been saying, and then he rubbed his head as if he were puzzled, and did not exactly understand her. He then spoke as follows:

'Well, aunt, all this is very strange that you have been telling me. I thought poetry was only a string of verses, with rhymes at the end of them, such as *hop top*, *butter mutter*, *eater Peter*, &c. I have made some verses myself, and I thought these were poetry, and pretty good poetry too.'

'Well,' said his aunt, 'Let me hear your verses, and I will then tell you whether they are poetry or not.' 'I will repeat them all,' said Jack, 'If you will promise not to laugh.' 'Go on,' said his aunt, 'I shall not laugh if I can help it.' Jack then proceeded as follows:

'The dog sat down to eat his bone,
The cat went out to walk alone,
The bird was singing on the bough,
The bell was tinkling on the cow.

The leaves were all upon the trees,
    The grass was on the ground,
The butterfly was on the breeze,—
    A pint doth weigh a pound.

A ghost was walking in a lane,
    'T was night, and all was still,
A fly was on the window-pane,
    The pigs did want their swill!'

When he got to this point, his aunt Mary laughed outright, and Jack declared that she had broken her promise, and he would not repeat another verse. He sat for some time with a pouting and offended air. At length his aunt went on to speak in the following manner: 'I hope you will excuse me, dear Jack, for laughing, but I could not well help it. Your idea of poetry is like that of other children, and I think your first attempt is quite as successful as that of most persons.'

CONCLUSION

Soon after the period of his life which I have described to you, he went to school, where he attended closely to the instruction he received, and continued his habits of inquiring and thinking until he became distinguished above all his companions. When he left school, he had to get his living by trade, and the greater part of his time was occupied. But as he persevered in observing and thinking, and in reading whenever he had suitable leisure, he at last became a wise and learned man.

I have been anxious to set the example of Inquisitive Jack before you, because he pursued knowledge successfully with very little assistance from others. A boy may have the best books and the best teachers in the world, but unless he is willing to learn, and ready to exert the faculties he has, they will all do him no good.

It is no doubt a great advantage to have good teachers, and a great disadvantage to have none at all. It may not be in the power of every one to become learned, but every one may learn a great deal if he will make the most of the means within his reach. There are not many amongst my little readers who cannot command as many advantages as Jack possessed. There are not many who have not some kind friend or relation who would be ready, like Jack's aunt, to answer their questions, and encourage them in their progress; and there are none to whom the woods and the fields, the waters and the earth, the clouds and the starry sky are not open; who have not hands and eyes, and the other senses, with powers of thinking, too, if they would but exercise them. These, with the reading of a few books (which almost every one in this country may either obtain for himself or borrow) were the helps which Jack used, which tended to make him useful and respected amongst his friends, and furnished him with a never-ending source of pure enjoyment.

I shall now give you a few cautions respecting the reading of books. You should not try to read *many* books. It is an excellent thing to have read a few books well; but it is a bad thing to have read a great many hastily. It may be no disgrace to a person not to have read a book, but it is a certain disgrace to have read a book and to have learned nothing from it. A great many people are proud to boast that they have read many books: but this is a sad delusion. The important question is not—What books have you read? but—What do you know, and what use can you make of your knowledge?

You should learn one thing well, that is, get a good clear notion of it, before you learn another. Jack never overlooked this caution when he was

old enough to see its importance. He learned *one* thing at a time, and therefore he learned a great many things one after another, and he learned them all well. While he was studying a subject, his whole attention was fixed on it till he had become master of it; and thus it was that though he was acquainted with a variety of subjects, he was not a mere smatterer in anything.

By a smatterer, I do not mean merely one who knows a little of a subject: we must all of us know a little before we can know a great deal of any subject. A child who knows his alphabet only, knows but little but he is not a smatterer if he knows it well. I will tell you what a smatterer is. He is one who does not know any one part of a subject thoroughly but who seems to know something by having learned a few names and forms which he uses in conversation, without being acquainted with their proper meaning.

I have now, in conclusion, only one short piece of advice to give you. If you wish to be learned and wise, apply your whole mind to one thing at a time; never try to *appear* to know more than you really do; and however learned and wise you may be, do not set yourself up, but be humble, and remember that there have been many more wise and learned than you are, and that what gifts you have were given you to use to the good of your fellow men and the glory of your Creator.

⁂

THE AFRICAN MONITOR GIRL

A SHIP was on the sea, not far from the shores of Africa. It was not full of sugar, cotton, oil or anything of the kind. It was crowded with black men, women, and children, who had been stolen from their homes, and were now being carried to a distant land, there to be sold as slaves. These poor people were cruelly used; they were bound with chains to the decks, and very little food was given them to eat.

But an English ship came that way, and seized the slave vessel. The iron chains were then taken off their limbs, and the poor blacks were carried to a place in West Africa, called Free Town. There they soon found happy homes, and Christian teachers.

Among those who were thus saved from slavery were a black man and his wife, with their little girl. They settled in a spot where they could hear about the Lord Jesus Christ, and their child was sent to a school. The teachers

gave her the name of Charlotte Bell. It is thought she was so called after the name of some lady in England, who paid the money for her support.

Many of the black children are quick in learning; but it was not so with Charlotte. At first she could not learn at all, but she tried very much, and that was the right way. It is the right way for *you*, young friend.

After some time, Charlotte got on very nicely with her lessons.

Four or five years passed away, and she had so much improved in learning that she was made a monitor, and used to assist in teaching some of her little dark-faced companions.

But her time for labour was short. Some have only a short day of labour; and this should teach us all to do what we ought to do without delay. At the age of fifteen, Charlotte was taken

ill, when a missionary went to see her.

Charlotte told him that, while lying at home, she had seen more of her sinful state before God than she had seen before, and had sought Jesus her Saviour with all her heart. 'Oh, yes,' she said, 'it is good for me that I have been brought low. I have learned to know God: I have learned to love Jesus.'

As she lay in the poor hut from week to week, she was always found with the Bible on her bed, and she told all who came to see her how glad she was that she had been taught to read it.

Although very weak, and in much pain, a murmur was not heard from her lips: she was always grateful for every little kindness done for her. Her great delight was in reading the Scriptures and in prayer.

The day before Charlotte Bell died, she called her mother and said, 'When I am gone, you must not be sorry: nobody must cry. I do not want you to put on a black dress for me; you should all have white, because I am going to a happy place. The next morning, before the sun shone into the little window of her hut, she wished her father to pray for her. She then spoke aloud the hymn which begins—

'How did my heart rejoice to hear
   My friends devoutly say,
In Zion let us all appear,
   And keep the solemn day!'

Charlotte now lay very quiet, and in a few hours she died.

When the people took her body to the grave, the girls and boys of the school walked after the coffin, and wept as they saw it laid in the ground.

We should do what we can to help those who carry the gospel to other lands. Had it not been for kind Christian teachers, Charlotte Bell would have died a poor heathen girl.

ON SEEING THE BIBLE SOCIETY'S NEW COLLECTING BOX

It must have been sweet music
   That woke the still starlight,
When angels sang of Jesus,
   On the first Christmas night.

And now the gracious message
   By men is borne to men;
A child may swell the chorus
   That angels joined in then.

MY FIRST
LESSON BOOK
TO TEACH ME
SPELLING AND READING.

ILLUSTRATED BY

FORTY ENGRAVINGS.

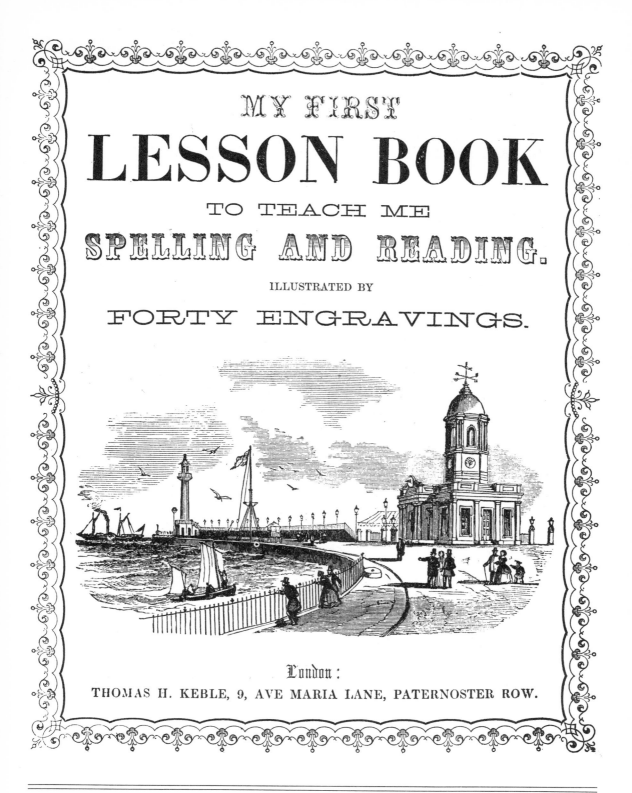

London:
THOMAS H. KEBLE, 9, AVE MARIA LANE, PATERNOSTER ROW.

ABCD
EFGH
IJKL
MNOP
QRST
UVW
XYZ

ab	eb	ib		ob	ub	al
ac	ec	ic		oc	uc	el
ad	ed	id		od	ud	il
af	ef	if		of	uf	ol
ag	eg	ig		og	ug	ul
am	em	im		om	um	at
an	en	in		on	un	et

ba	be	bi		bo	bu	by
ca	ce	ci		co	cu	cy
da	de	di		do	du	dy
fa	fe	fi		fo	fu	fy
ga	ge	gi		go	gu	gy
ha	he	hi		ho	hu	hy
ja	je	ji		jo	ju	jy

As we go	He is in	Is he up
As we go	*He is in*	*Is he up*
So we go	Is he in	Go we in
So we go	*Is he in*	*Go we in*

Be it so

Be it so

We go in

We go in

Ye do so

Ye do so

Oh me

Oh me

try to be still	*try to be still*

1 2 3 4 5 6 7 8 9 0

1 2 3 4 5 6 7 8 9 0

THE DEATH AT SCHOOL
True Sketches from Life

PRAYERS were just concluded at Mrs O's school, and the young ladies were replacing their Bibles preparatory to retiring to rest, when a letter was brought in for a little girl named Susan. It was from her parents; and that it contained good news, might be read in the joyful expression which the little girl's face assumed whilst she read it. Hastening to Mrs O. with her fair face flushed, and her eyes sparkling with joy, she said eagerly, 'This is a letter from mamma, and I am to go home to-morrow, for papa is recalled to India, and as mamma goes with him they will not leave me behind.' Mrs O. felt very sorry at the thought of parting with Susan; for during two years at school, her conduct had been such, as to lead Mrs O. to indulge the hope of her being one of the fold of Christ; but she felt also, that all things are ordered rightly, though not always according to our wishes. Mrs O. was one who anxiously desired the religious improvement of those committed to her care, and for this end she laboured and prayed, and God had hitherto blessed her prayers in a great degree. She now led Susan into another parlour, and talked long and seriously to her, pointing out the many means she would have of teaching others the truth as it is in Jesus. Then, after praying with and for her, she sent her to rejoin her companions. When Susan entered the school-room all her playmates looked very kindly at her, and some said, 'How happy Susan looks to-night!' and others, 'It is the thought of going home to-morrow.' But Susan soon now checked them, by calling them all together, and distributing to each some memento of her affection. 'Keep this for my sake,' was many times repeated, whilst she seemed struggling between joy and sorrow; yet tears would fill her eyes, and the fervent 'God bless you!' and kiss to each of her loved companions, showed how dear they were to her.

It was near day-break, on the following morning, when Susan was suddenly taken ill, and alarmed her companions with cries for aid; and in a short time after, that house where lately the stillness of night had reigned, became the scene of confusion and dismay. But doubt was soon followed by certainty, and we were told that Susan was in glory even before the morning sun had shed its first rays on earth. All that human aid could do was done, but her death arose from a complaint of the heart, which no

power on earth could avert. Before mid-day her parents arrived, and ere the sun had set, the remains of Susan were removed from our sight for ever.

May I ask my young readers if they also are ready? Ye know not in what day or hour the Son of man cometh, and death may come to you as suddenly as it did to this dear child, and find you unprepared. Many who read this, I doubt not, have been to a boarding-school, and know the anxiety and eager hope with which the holidays are looked forward to by all. How many the preparations made for home! How constantly the words 'When I am at home' escape your lips! How carefully your attention has been given to various studies! You look, you wish for no other reward beyond the love and approbation of your parents. If the love of earth is so eagerly sought after, if an earthly home is thus looked forward to and prepared for, how much more should you seek those things which are above! an habitation eternal in the heavens, an abode for ever in happiness, to live for ever in the presence of God, and to have his love and protection granted to those who ask for it on earth; surely these things are worth striving for; the love of our Father in heaven is indeed worth seeking; and what excuse have ye, if ye neglect so great a salvation?

THE VULGAR LITTLE LADY

'But, mamma, now,' said Charlotte, 'pray
    don't you believe
  That I'm better than Jenny, my nurse?
  Only see my red shoes, and the lace on my
    sleeve;
  Her clothes are a thousand times worse.'

'Gentility, Charlotte,' her mother replied,
  'Belongs to no station or place;
And nothing's so vulgar as folly and pride,
  Though dress'd in red slippers and lace.'

NEGLIGENT MARY

Ah, Mary! what, do you for dolly not care?
  And why is she left on the floor?
Forsaken, and covered with dust, I declare;
  With you I must trust her no more.

Suppose now—for Mary is *dolly* to me,
  Whom I love to see tidy and fair—
Suppose I should leave you, as dolly I see,
  In tatters, and comfortless there.

And therefore it is, in my Mary I strive
  To check every fault that I see;
Mary's doll is but waxen—mamma's is alive,
  And of far more importance than she.

LITTLE ANN AND HER MAMMA

Little Ann and her mother were walking
  one day
  Through London's wide city so fair;
And business obliged them to go by the way
  That led them through Cavendish Square.

'Mamma,' said the child, 'see that carriage
  so fair,
  All cover'd with varnish and gold;
Those ladies are riding so charmingly there,
  While we have to walk in the cold.'

'Look there, little girl,' said her mother, 'and
  see
  What stands at that very coach door!
A poor ragged beggar; and listen how she
  A halfpenny tries to implore.

'This poor little beggar is hungry and cold,
　　No mother awaits her return;
And while such an object as this you behold,
　　Your heart should with gratitude burn.

'Your house and its comforts, your food and
　　your friends,
　　'Tis favour in God to confer;
Have you any claim to the bounty He sends?
　　Who makes you to differ from her?'

GOOD NATURE

Two good little children, named Mary and
　　Ann,
Both happily live, as good girls always can;
And though they are not either sullen or mute,
They seldom or never are heard to dispute.

If one wants a thing that the other would
　　like—
Well, what do they do? Must they quarrel
　　and strike?
No: each is so willing to give up her own,
That such disagreements are there never
　　known.

THE DISAPPOINTMENT

In tears to her mother poor Harriet came:
　　Let us listen to hear what she says:
'Oh, see, dear mamma, it is pouring with rain,
　　We cannot go out in the chaise.'

'I'm sorry, my dear,' her kind mother replied,
　　'The rain disappoints us to-day;
But sorrow still more that you fret for a ride
　　In such an extravagant way!'

OLD SARAH

Old Sarah everybody knows,
Nor is she pitied as she goes—
　　A melancholy sight.
For people do not like to give
Relief to those who idle live,
　　And work not when they might.

ABOUT UGLY IDOLS

PERHAPS you ask, what is an idol? I will tell you. It is nothing at all in the world, but a piece of wood or stone, and yet, where the black people live, they say prayers to them. You might as well pray to your whipping top or to a stone in the wall.

This is a picture of a place where some of them keep their idols, which they call a temple. If you look at it you will see three great ugly idols, with great staring eyes. They are made of logs of wood and painted red and yellow, and are so very ugly that they are enough to frighten any one to look at them. And yet thousands of people come hundreds of miles once a year to pray to these stupid things.

And as it is very hot in that country, many of the men and women fall down and die on the road as they are going or coming back. If a poor man falls down on the road in England, the first that comes past will try to help him, but there they never do. He is left to die alone. And what is worse, the wild dogs and great birds will begin to eat him before he is quite dead. This is very shocking. Sometimes mothers will take their little girls or boys many miles to see these ugly idols. Some years ago, a good man went to

see this place where the idols are. There were many thousands of people there, and a great crowd stood round the temple. As there are so many, there is often want of food, or the cholera takes them, and they die in a few hours. When they die they do not bury them, but drag them out to the sands, where dogs and birds eat them. That good man went to look at the place, but it almost made him sick to see it. There he saw a little girl, nine years old, sitting crying near her dead mother, and trying to drive the dogs and birds away. He asked her where her home was, and she said she had no home but where her mother was. Only think of that, no home but there among bones, and skulls, and dead bodies. It is very likely that poor child would soon die too, for no one would care for her.

I have told you of these sad things that you may be very thankful to God that you were not born there, or you might have been left, like that poor black girl, without father or mother, or house or home. And I have told you that you may see what sorrows come when men and women forsake the living God, to pray to dumb idols that are nothing at all in the world, and cannot help them. And I have told you, too, that you may feel pity for those poor black boys and girls who live where there are no sabbath days, no bibles, and no teachers, and so do not know God, or Jesus Christ whom he sent to save us.

Many good people now give their money to send bibles and teachers to them. The teacher who goes is called a mis-sion-ary. English boys and girls ought to help to send teachers, by putting a penny now and then into the mission box. Thousands of boys and girls in England do so now, and though they only give a penny now and then, it comes to a deal of money in one year. And their money is not lost. It does a great deal of good in helping to teach poor black children, many of whom have been taught to fear the great God, and love Jesus Christ, and have died happy; and no doubt if we go to heaven we shall find many of them there. Should you not be glad to go to heaven yourself, and when you get there find many of those poor black children there too, who will then be as fair and as happy as you, and sing with you the praises of Jesus for ever. Oh, that will be joyful! So always, as long as you live, do all you can for missions, that the people all over the world may burn their stupid wooden idols, and learn to pray to the living God, and hear about the love of the Lord Jesus, who died for their sins, that they might go to heaven.

In a carriage droll
To the gates did roll
Our little friend, sweet Silverhair;
In her little coach borne
Up to the green lawn
Push'd along by a comical bear.

At sweet Silverhair, how the party did stare,
When they saw her approach with her servant the bear;
She smiled on them all, as she walked to her seat,
And the Queen of the Fairies the damsel did greet.

Three times 7 are **Twenty-one** Ducks, swimming in a pond:
Three times 8 are **Twenty-four** Geese, in the yard beyond.
Three times 9 are **Twenty-seven** little Pigs at play.
Three times 10 are **Thirty** Men and Women making Hay.
Three times 11 are **Thirty-three** black Ravens in the air,
Three times 12 are **Thirty-six** Pears—touch them, if you dare.

Four times 4 are **Sixteen** People, dancing a new Quadrille;
Four times 5 are **Twenty** Ladies who are sitting still.
Four times 6 are **Twenty-four** Lights in a Chandelier,
Four times 7 are **Twenty-eight** Musicians, as 'tis clear.

Four times 8 are **Thirty-two** great Nobles at a feast,
Four times 9 are **Thirty-six** fine dishes, at the least.
Four times 10 are **Forty** Bottles of the choicest Sherry;
Four times 11 are **Forty-four** Glasses of Brandy-Cherry,
Four times 12 are **Forty-eight** good Songs, to make them merry.

HARRY'S RASH WISH,
AND HOW THE FAIRIES GRANTED IT

Chapter I

HARRY DISLIKES BABIES

'I hate babies! I wish there were no such things in the world!' cried little Harry Thompson, as, having finished his first inspection of the new owner of the nursery cot, he tripped across the floor with his little bare feet and climbed into bed. 'I wish, nurse, you'd take that nasty cradle out of the room, and bring back my rocking-horse instead.'

'Indeed, Master Harry, I ain't a-goin' to do nothing of the kind, and I am ashamed of you, that I am, speakin' in such a heartless way of your little sister,' replied nurse, reproachfully; 'it is not so many years ago since you were a-rocking in the same cradle yourself, and a very peevish, cross little baby you were—always a-screamin' or a-whinin' at summat or other.'

'I am sure I was never half so red, or so ugly, or so small,' cried Harry, taking his fairy-tale book from the head of his little wooden crib, and thrusting it under his pillow. 'What good are babies? They can't fight, or kill lions or tigers or buffaloes, or read fairy-tale books, or do anything useful.'

'I can't say as how I see much use in readin' the silly stuff as is printed now-a-days in fairy-tale books,' replied nurse, rather contemptuously; 'and if I was you, Master Harry, I'd be thinking of saying my prayers when I put my head down on the pillow, instead of gabbling about hobgoblins and such-like.'

'Hobgoblins and fairies are not one scrap like each other; so there you are wrong, nurse,' cried Harry triumphantly. 'Hobgoblins are like ghosts—indeed, they are generally ghosts, with long white sheets and green eyes, and very hideous; but fairies are most beautiful things, with wings, and yellow hair, and shining dresses, and wands, and they can come in and out of a room, and make people invisible, or do anything they like.'

'I wish, then, they'd make you invisible, Master Harry, or do something with you to keep you quiet, for there's not much chance of the baby sleepin' while you keep up such a chatter and nonsense. Put your head down on your pillow now, and don't let me hear another word till the mornin'.'

After this admonition from nurse there was silence in the nursery for a few minutes; but until Harry was actually asleep he could seldom cease talking, and presently he began again in a kind of loud whisper, 'I wish—I wish—oh! how I do wish something.'

'What do you wish, Master Harry? Is it a slice of the cake that I have in the press?' asked nurse, who, after all, was not an unkindly soul; and she rose and walked towards the cupboard.

'No, no, I did not mean the cake—though I should like a bit of that very much; but I wish so much I could be a fairy just for one night—only for a single night—and then I know what I should do.'

'What would you do?'

And nurse, having cut a slice fom the cake, placed it in Harry's outstretched hand.

'I would turn all the babies in the world into mice or rats or butter, as the enchanter did to the Queen and her children in the golden bower, and then cats would eat them, and people would catch them, and soon there would be no more of them, and I should have my rocking-horse back in the nursery, instead of that nasty cradle.'

'Well, well, if ever I heard such an idea!' murmured nurse to herself with a smile; 'a-turnin' of babies into mice and suchlike. I doubt but you'd be repentin' of your wish after a bit if the fairies were just to take you at your word.'

This speech of nurse's hardly reached Harry's ears, for, having finished his cake, he was already half-way into the land of dreams. He tried to answer her, but could not, and though his eyes were still blinking a little, and he could hear the singing of the kettle on the hob, yet he had an uncomfortable vision of seeing the baby crawl slowly out of the cradle on to the floor, and, having looked all around it furtively, suddenly creep up the side of the nursery press, and disappear, squeezing itself through the well-known mouse-hole, out of which Harry had that very day picked the piece of cork placed there by Lizzie the housemaid.

Very deeply little Harry slept, with his head pressed into his pillow and his arm thrust under it, holding in loving embrace his much-prized fairy-tale book. Had he not slept so very soundly, he might perhaps have seen—or, perhaps, indeed, even in his sleep he did see—

the fairies one by one, as the clock struck twelve, creeping out between the leaves of his book and climbing over the side of his bed, letting themselves stealthily down upon the floor.

And such a strange lot as they were, to be sure! enchanters and witches and gnomes, and lots of old well-known friends, such as Ali Baba and the Forty Thieves, and the Yellow Dwarf, and Beauty and the Beast walking arm-in-arm, and Cinderella, whose train was carried by her two sisters, and at the head of the procession little Snow White, whose mother had so long wished that she might be born, and when she was born she was so lovely—oh, so lovely!— Harry could hardly take his eyes off her.

Then some strange kind of ceremony began. Harry grew quite terrified, and crept back under the clothes; and he knew that all the gnomes and creatures were creeping up the side of his bed again as fast as ever they could, in great hurry and confusion.

Chapter II

THE FAIRIES GRANT HARRY'S WISH

It was a bitterly cold morning, a red foggy sun, and the ground covered with may inches of snow, when at length Harry, having yawned and stretched himself many scores of times, opened his eyes and thought to himself that it was perhaps time to get up. The sleet was drifting against the unshuttered windows, the room was grey and gloomy inside also, but in the yard beneath the cocks were crowing lustily, proclaiming aloud, in no faltering tones, that though the day was dull, it was time to be up and stirring.

But how was this? some one must have changed the stockings he wore yesterday, and put another pair full of holes under his pillow, for the moment he thrust his foot into one of them, out came both his toe and heel through the sole, and the ribbed top came off with such a jerk in his hands, that it threw him right back upon his pillow.

'Who on earth can have played such a silly trick?' cried Harry, as he indignantly kicked the foot of the stocking over the edge of the bed, 'especially when I have only to walk across the room to the press to get out another pair.' And Harry, regardless of the cold, clambered out of his bed upon the floor, and crossed the room towards the old oak press which held the children's linen. 'But I say,' shivered Harry, as he gazed around him in some bewilderment, 'Lizzie has not even lit the fire yet: I never saw the grate look so black and empty; and what can have become of the cradle?'

The press was usually locked; but this morning the press stood open—indeed, it seemed to have got some kind of wrench, for it hung forward and downward, as if depending from a single hinge.

'Gracious me! what on earth has nurse been doing?—why, the press is nearly empty!' cried Harry. 'Why, what has become of my new knickerbocker suit, and all my other things? they could not be rolled up in this filthy bundle.' And Harry thrust his hand into the corner of the middle shelf, where there seemed to be a heap of some mouldy clothes; but quickly as he pushed in his hand, he drew it quicker forth, for out rushed first a huge fat mouse with a long horny tail, and immediately afterwards such a host of woodlice and earwigs as made Harry spring several paces back from the press, and shake his little night-dress frantically, to free

74

himself from the host of unpleasant living creatures that had suddenly fallen upon it.

'Nurse! nurse!' cried poor Harry in great dismay and distress, 'what has happened to the press? some one has taken all our nice clothes out, and put in a lot of dirty rubbish! Nurse, you must awake and get up! Nurse, nurse! do you hear? I'm calling you.'

But there was no responsive sound from the bed: nurse must have been in a very sound sleep, for she never stirred, or even turned round at poor Harry's terrified appeal; and only for a faint whining sound, like the waking yawn of his new-born sister, Harry would have thought that nurse must be already up.

So Harry, shivering and shuddering, sat upon his heels and gazed earnestly into the darkness, trying to make out the exact position of nurse and baby in the bed; but by-and-by, as he could see things a little clearer, it seemed to him that he must be mistaken as to nurse's being asleep, for he was certain he saw her eyes wide open and staring at him in a horrible glaring kind of way, which made his blood, cold as it was already, run like ice through his veins.

'What's the matter, nurse?' he asked, timidly; 'why are you staring at me in that way? Nurse—nurse! why don't you answer me? You are frightening me on purpose; it's very unkind of you.' And at last, with a cry born both of fear and anger, Harry tore back the curtain of the bed with one sudden wrench, and beheld— oh, horrible sight!—neither his nurse nor little sister asleep upon their pillows, but in their place a large tabby cat, gazing steadily at him

with scared eyeballs, from a heap of dirty feathers, and surrounded by a mewing circle of tabby kittens.

For a moment or so Harry seemed uncertain what to do: surprise, fear, utter bewilderment, kept him rooted to the spot, while a host of vague questions rushed through his mind. What had happened? where was he? was he in his own nursery at all? had he wandered in his sleep into some strange house? for even the chairs and tables in the room, he now remarked, were absent from their usual places.

It would be well for him to find out whether he was in his own home or not; one glance out of the window would be sufficient for him to recognize the garden, with its pretty circular flower bed and close-clipped yew hedges; and giving one frightened glance at the cat, whose eyes seemed to follow all his movements, Harry crawled back over the footboard and approached the window.

Yes, it was his own house: there were the mountains opposite, the familiar windmill on the top of the peak, and the great pine wood in the cleft of the hill. But where was the summer-house? Harry could not see it, though he strained his eyes across the snow till they ached: it seemed to him as if the branches of the lilac-trees must have grown ever so much taller, for they hid it quite from his view; even the very garden-seats of rustic wood were missing from their shady corners, and everything had a strange uncared-for look which the unusual amount of snow could not account for.

Chapter III

GREAT CHANGES

Harry hurried down the narrow vestibule passage to the hall door. Judging by the noise of nibbling, scratching, scrabbling, and skirmishing about in the passage, the mice seemed to be holding an early parliament, but all fled at the sound of the boy's eager footsteps, and no impediment presented itself till Harry actually stood outside, knee-deep in the cold snow which lay heaped up in the vestibule.

Here, indeed, he did pause, poor child, and looked around him in dismay and utter bewilderment. He did not even seem to feel the cold, or to be sensible of the scantiness of his attire; his whole mind had evidently become absorbed in the endeavour to take in the extraordinary position of everything around him, and to arrive at some conclusions as to how it had all happened.

First, right across his path lay one of the great stone pillars which supported the portico; another, though not actually fallen, leaned in a helpless way against its neighbour; and the portico itself in many places seemed crumbled and fallen away. Nor was this the only token of ruin and disaster. The staunch oak-tree, between whose branches hung the children's swing, and at whose base was built the circular seat, so secluded and sociable, lay also on its side—a fallen giant, with the snow piled high on its gnarled roots; and the very wall which bounded the pleasure-ground itself seemed nothing now but an irregular heap of stones, with great gaps leading out upon the highway.

He was obliged to rest himself, sitting down on the old stone trough by the pump, for his knees trembled, his feet ached with the cold, and the sleet, which was still falling in long slanting lines from the heavy clouds above, seemed to cut him through and through.

How long he sat there, leaning his poor tired head against the iron handle, he could not tell; the cold had so numbed him, he did not care to move, and the thought of returning to the empty desolate house was more dreadful to him than anything else. All the long morning not one soul had entered the yard, usually alive with workmen, and resounding with cheery farm-sounds of the flail, or the whetting of the scythe, or the tinkle of the milk-cans. Not a human footstep had been heard in the lane close beside him, or the whistle of a passer-by. Supposing he were to wander a little way down the road; and see if all were changed in the outer world, as in his own home and his own house?

So at length, the sun being now on the decline and the darkness coming on with giant strides, Harry rose from beside the pump and walked straight out through the gap in the hedge into the lane beyond. This lane led to the main road on the one side, and right up the mountain on the other; something determined him to choose the more secluded of the two roads, and without further delay he turned, tired as he was, and breasted the furzy hill.

It was a puff of blue smoke curling up from a distant cabin roof on the mountainside that had attracted poor Harry's attention, and made hope stir suddenly in his breast. Had he not often read in books before now of lost children, poor wandering babes, being called back to life and energy by the sight of just such a wreath of pale smoke emerging from a hut where lived some good old dame or tender-hearted ruffian? He quickened his pace, and passed on through the still drifting snow and increasing darkness to the cottage on the moor. Not one living soul did he meet on all this long and toilsome walk. All the cabins by the roadside were deserted, and most of them in ruins.

At last Harry came in full view of the cabin. No light burned as yet within its window, but still up from the chimney issued a ghostly, cloud of smoke. Harry now having reached the longed for goal, almost feared to advance farther. What if out of the darkness were to spring some creature more terrible than the darkness itself— some evil gnome or black enchanter? Gathering up all the courage left within his little perished frame, Harry pushed open the gate that separated the cabin from the road, and, going up the narrow path, knocked timidly at the door.

At first there was no answer; but at last there was a stir, a kind of groan, and a trembling voice cried querulously, 'Eh! what's that?— what's that a-knockin' itself against the door. I cannot rise to see. Be off with you, whate'er you are, and do not come troublin' me more.'

But Harry could not turn back now. If he did not find the rest and shelter he had so long toiled for, he felt he must lie down and die. Once again, therefore, Harry knocked, and pushing against the door with all his force, it slowly yielded to his pressure, the rusty hinges creaked, the panels groaned at the unusual strain put upon them, but still the opening grew wider and wider, till at length he stood inside the portal, trying with dazed eyes and beating heart to fathom the darkness within.

That there was some living inhabitant of the cabin he could not doubt; he had heard the voice, and he could even distinguish already something in shape and form like a human being crouching on a bench by the side of a waning fire. Whatever it was, let it be man or woman, witch or enchanter, the opening of the door did not seem to make any impression upon it, for there was no movement of surprise, or raising of the angry querulous voice he had heard when outside. All the energies of the strange being seemed centred about the fire, for as Harry still looked earnestly in its direction, he could see two long shrivelled arms stretched out over the embers, and the head bent low down almost to the knees, as if to draw in with its breath the dull heat emitted by the dying fire.

A sudden leap of flame in the grate revealed

still more clearly the outlines of the figure before him. And a strange figure it was, with shoulders twisted and distorted, a long grey beard hanging almost to its very feet as it leaned forward, and matted locks of white hair, which nearly hid from sight a face wrinkled and yellow like a withered apple.

Harry would have made his escape now if he could, but he could not; his numbed feet and legs seemed to have lost all power of movement, and he stood opposite the old man, as if frozen to the spot, gazing into the fire in an agony of fright.

Chapter IV

A VERY OLD MAN

There was something curiously simple in the face of the old man, as he sat gazing at Harry in a sort of amazement, and tears came up into his dim eyes and ran down his cheeks. At this Harry seemed to lose all fear, and he began to question his companion; but he received to all his questions never an answer, save that the old man drew him nearer and nearer, muttering to himself, 'A hundred years—ay, a hundred years since I saw the like; a hundred years since I saw a face like thine;' and so on, the same words, it might be a score of times.

'Since you saw what?' asked Harry at length.

'The like o' thee—the like o' thee; I have not seen the face of a child like thee for nigh a hundred year. Why, dear heart, one has not seen the smilin' face o' a babe i' this wicked world for a hundred year—and a lonesome world it has been without them; all the bright laughs, and the innocent tears, and the pretty dimples in their cheeks all gone, all flown away in the little babies: it was a'most enough to break one's heart, to see all the empty cradles a-standin' by the fireside, and the mothers a-walkin' about wi' nothin' i' their arms, and no song of love in their mouths, instead o' singing their wee ones to sleep on their breasts wi' sweet songs and kisses.'

'I don't understand what you mean,' said Harry plaintively; 'why, I am not very old, and I have seen hundreds and thousands of children and babies. Why, I have a little sister of my own who is only a few days old.'

'Then, if that be so,' replied the old man, gloomily, 'thou must have dropped into a strange world in the middle o' the night, for not one babe has been born in this world of ours for a hundred years, since the night when the fairies walked abroad i' the fields and houses, and granted many a wicked wish to them as had wicked wishes i' their mouths and hearts.'

'When was that?—tell me more about it all,' asked Harry eagerly, as some dim recollection came creeping over his mind, which made him feel unhappy and ill at ease. 'When did all this happen?'

'It happened o' a night—let me see, ay, it happened just a hundred years ago, come last

night. The fairies, they say, do fly in swarms o' nights when the moon is at her full, and play their pranks all over the earth, and then they come creepin' at dead o' night into the houses, and makin' such mischief as is in their power to make, granting to silly folk their silly wishes, and harmin' those besides who never harm them. However, as I heard tell, for I was but a lad then, just turned o' fifteen—ay, you may look at me wi' your wide-open eyes in wonder, lad, for a hundred and fifteen years old I am this blessed day. But to finish what I had in my mind to tell you. One of these nights, with the big moon a-glowin' in the sky overhead, a host of them walked in at twelve o' the clock to a house down yon i' the valley, where there lived, I heard tell, an honest gentleman and his wife and some little folk.'

'Go on—go on,' urged Harry, 'I must hear it all.'

'Well, an thou must, thou must,' replied the old man sadly; 'there was a wee chap had fallen asleep i' his cot, with some foolish wish in his mouth, as how he would there were no more babies i' the world, or something o' the kind, and like a poor innocent lamb he bleated out

his idle fancy to some one who sat by him, and the fairies, who were a-clustering round his head, caught up the very words as he spake them; and so, as I was told, they not only carried out his silly babbling words, but they made away wi' the poor child himself, at least his cot was empty next morning, and though his father and mother hunted the world up and down, they never saw his pretty face again. Some said as how the nurse was to blame, for she had wished the fairies would make the little chap invisible; but, be that as it may, they never saw him more—never, never.'

'What was the boy's name?' asked Harry, in a voice so low, so sad, so trembling, it would never have reached the old man's ears had it not been so full of pain.

'His name—nay, I misdoubt if I can call it to mind, but bide a bit and I will try. Ay, ay, I mind it now, I mind it now; his name was—'

But before the words could leave the old man's lips, Harry leaped from the bench with a scream; his pain was too great to bear any longer, his agony of mind too keen for endurance. 'Don't say it was Harry, don't say it was me!' he shrieked, with such bitterness, that the old man seemed to shrink and wither away from before his sight, the walls of the cabin rocked, the snow seemed to hiss outside in its fury, and then some one shouted into Harry's ears with a voice which sounded like a peal of thunder,

'Awake, Master Harry! awake, it is time for you to get up, you have slept quite long enough!'

Ay, one would think so; a hundred years is a good long sleep for a little boy of five years old;

and as Harry awoke and rubbed his eyes in utter bewilderment as to where he was, where was he, think you? Why, in his own snug nursery: the fire was burning brightly in the shining grate; the kettle, not the snow, was hissing on the hob; the tea was made already, and slices of nice white bread and butter were cut and temptingly laid upon a plate; the cradle was in a corner by the fire; nurse, singing happily, sat plying the rockers with her foot: how cosy, how bright, how comfortable they all looked!

And so our old friend Harry had his breakfast in bed, Lizzie gave it to him on a little tray, and nurse laughed as she poured out his tea, and said he must have been dreaming in the night, he tumbled about so, and screeched like, and she did not wish to rouse him in the morning, as he seemed to have fallen into an easier sleep.

And so he had been dreaming, poor Harry, though he did not tell nurse what the terrible dream was all about; but, when he was washed and dressed, and his curls were all combed out and smoothed, before he left the nursery he paused and leaned over the little pink-lined cradle where his sister lay fast asleep, and looking at her for a long time, he stooped down and gave her such a kiss on her little dimpled cheek, that nurse looked up in amazement; but Harry in his heart knew why.

QUEEN VICTORIA AND THE BIBLE

An African prince sent an ambassador to our honoured and beloved Queen Victoria. He brought with him costly presents, which she was asked to accept, and in return to tell him the secret of England's greatness. The Queen did not give him a list of the colonies she possessed; she did not tell him how many soldiers she had; how many ships she could command; nor the amount of her revenue. She did not, like King Hezekiah, display before him in a boastful spirit her treasures, the crown jewels. No, but handing him a well-bound copy of the Bible, she said, 'Tell the Prince that *this* is the secret of England's greatness!' Was not that a good answer, and worthy the Queen of Bible-loving England? And she was right, for it is the Bible that has made England great among the nations of the earth; and just in proportion as she reveres and obeys the Bible will she continue so.

A WELCOME GUEST FROM ROBIN'S NEST.

THE ROBINS' NEST

A pair of Robin Redbreasts build their nest in the wall of an orchard belonging to a kind gentleman named Benson, who will not allow little birds to be molested.

WELCOME GUESTS

The Robin Redbreasts, grown familiar by repeated favours, approach by degrees nearer and nearer to their little friends, and at length venture into the room, and feed upon the table.

FRIENDLY VISITORS

The little Bensons, Harriet and Frederick, feed the birds every morning; so the Robins soon come for their share, to carry to their little ones, Robin, Dicky, Flapsy, and Pecksy.

A 'MONSTER'

One day the nestlings declare that they have been frightened, in the absence of the old birds, by a dreadful monster. But it was only their kind friend the gardener!

THE GARDENER'S NEWS

Joe the gardener, having peeped into the nest, goes at once to tell Miss Harriet and Master Frederick what he has seen; and the children are greatly pleased at the news.

A CRUEL BOY

Master and Miss Jenkins come on a visit to the Bensons. Young Jenkins is a very cruel boy, who wishes to ill-use the dog and the cat, but Harriet is just in time to prevent him.

A PEEP AT THE NEST

Mrs. Benson allows the children to go to see the nest. Fred mounts the ladder first, and is delighted at seeing the four young ones; then his sister ventures up to take a peep.

A TENDER CHARGE

Now Master Jenkins had taken some young birds, which he had given to his sister; but Miss Jenkins resigns them to Harriet and Frederick, who gladly accept the charge.

A SURPRISE

The four little Robins, being now able to fly, leave the nest; and one day Harriet and Frederick, hearing a chirp, to their great delight come upon the whole family!

NEGLECTED FOR PETS

Mrs. Benson takes Harriet to see Mrs. Addis, a lady who gives all her care and affection to her pets, and neglects her little girl, who is shy and awkward with strangers.

ROBIN'S ACCIDENT

Robin, the eldest of the brood, disobeys his parents, and has a bad fall; so he is obliged to take refuge with Joe, the gardener, in the tool-house.

RELIEVING THE POOR

Harriet relieves the poor woman whose husband and family were in want, and whom Mrs. Benson had desired to call. The poor woman is very grateful for their kindness.

A TIDY PIGSTY

Mrs. Benson takes the children to Farmer Wilson's. They visit the pigsty, which they find clean and sweet. The pigs grunt and look as if they were pleased to see them.

THE WICKED WORLD

The little Redbreasts, having seen two bad boys climb a tree and take a nest of half-fledged linnets, and a family of thrushes, are quite content to remain safe in their orchard.

THE POULTRY YARD

Harriet and Freddy also visit the barnyard, where they are delighted at the sight of the ducks and geese; some swimming, some diving, and others routing in the mud.

A GILDED CAGE

The old birds take the little Redbreasts to a grand aviary, where they see all sorts of birds in captivity, and are convinced of the blessings of freedom.

CRUELTY PUNISHED

Miss Jenkins takes example from her friend Harriet, but her brother grows up to be a cruel man; and while inhumanly flogging his horse, is thrown to the ground and killed.

CONCLUSION

As for the Robins, when the young ones were able to shift for themselves, the parent birds gave them some good advice, and bade them a tender farewell. As Robin never quite got over his accident, he made his home with his kind young friends, Harriet and Frederick. And the old birds often visited them again in winter-time.

THE COTTAGE CHILD

WOULD you like to hear a true story of a little girl? It was a poor cottage at which I called. I was met at the door by the mother of the family. She asked me to come in, and then gave me the only chair in the room to sit on.

I was just seated, when a child, in a weak tone of voice, said, 'Dear mother, give me a cup of water.' And she held out her poor thin hand to take it.

'Is this little girl ill?' I asked. 'Oh yes,' said the mother, 'she has been kept to the house a long time.'

'Will it disturb her if I talk to her?' 'No, sir; she likes very much for any one to speak to her, when she is out of pain.'

I now sat by the side of the bed on which the child lay, and said, 'Well, my dear, I see you are very ill.' 'Yes, sir, I have been sick a long time; but mother thinks my sore foot is better now.'

'And does your foot hurt you very much?' 'At times it does, sir.'

'Can you sit up in bed?' 'No, sir, only when mother holds me.'

I now saw under the pillow a small Testament. It was much worn, as if some one had loved to read it. As I took it into my hand, I asked, 'Is this your book, my child?' 'Yes, sir.'

'Can you read it?' 'Oh, yes, sir.'

'Whom do you read about in this holy book?' 'I read about Jesus Christ.'

'Who is Jesus Christ?' 'He is the Son of God, sir.'

'Where is he now?' 'He is in heaven, sir.'

'And what does your good book tell you about Jesus Christ?' 'It says he came into the world to save sinners.'

'Who are sinners?' 'We are all sinners, sir.'

'Is that so? Do you think you are a sinner?' 'Oh, yes, sir.'

'Well, my dear child, what good does it do you to read this book?' 'Why, sir, when my foot hurts me very much, I cannot sleep. Then, when the candle is gone out, I get so tired, and I try to think about God, and how he sent his Son to save us. And then I think how Jesus must have loved us, that he should come into the world and die for us.'

'That is right, my dear child. You know also

89

how Jesus took little children in his arms, and blessed them.' 'Yes, sir; was not that kind?'

'It is very nice for you to have such thoughts as you lie awake in the night. Is it not, my dear child?' 'Yes, sir, while I am thinking, I forget my bad foot; then I fall asleep, and get some rest. When the light shines in the morning, I awake; then I get my Testament from under my pillow, and read it. And then I think I do love God, and that God loves me.'

While we were thus talking, the doctor came in. I waited for a short time, and then left the place; but I shall never forget the house, the mother, the broken chair, the worn Testament, and the sick child, with her soft voice and thin hands. I seem to see them now.

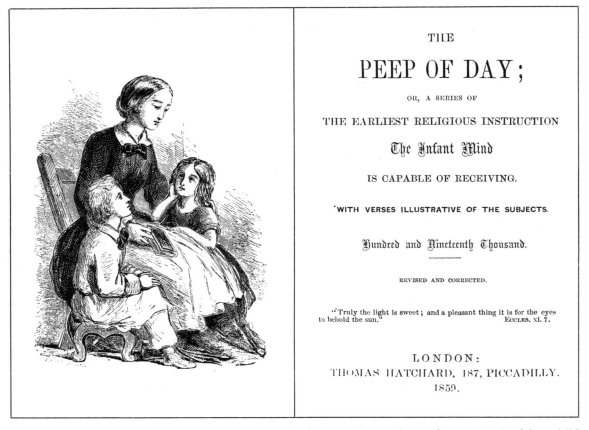

THE

PEEP OF DAY;

OR, A SERIES OF

THE EARLIEST RELIGIOUS INSTRUCTION

The Infant Mind

IS CAPABLE OF RECEIVING.

WITH VERSES ILLUSTRATIVE OF THE SUBJECTS.

Hundred and Nineteenth Thousand.

REVISED AND CORRECTED.

"Truly the light is sweet; and a pleasant thing it is for the eyes to behold the sun." ECCLES. xi. 7.

LONDON:
THOMAS HATCHARD, 187, PICCADILLY.
1859.

PREFACE

This little work aims to be the very least of all; —not in *size*, but in the humility of its contents. It aims at the superlative degree of littleness; and in this point seeks to resemble the least watch ever made,—the least picture ever painted,—the tiniest flower that ever grew. It desires to be among books, as the humming-bird among birds.

As soon as a child's mind is *capable* of receiving *systematic* instruction, this humble work attempts to convey it.

From a very early period a pious mother will, by *casual* remarks, endeavour to lead her child to the knowledge of his Creator and Redeemer; and in due time she will impart *systematic* instruction. It may be at *three* years of age—it may *not* be till *five*—that the child is prepared to listen to these little lessons. But—sooner or later—he will give evidence of his immortality by willingly hearkening to discourse concerning the INVISIBLE,—the ETERNAL,—the INFINITE.

The simplicity of the language may seem unworthy of the sublimity of the subject treated in these pages; and some may smile at the contrast;—but the little one will not smile—except with joy to hear of his Heavenly Father,

Family prayer at Thanksgiving Villa.

91

and of his incarnate Redeemer: for the merry inmates of the nursery are capable of tasting higher pleasures than toys and dainties can afford.

But there are children who have *no* nurseries. To them these instructions were first addressed, and into their SCHOOL-ROOMS this humble work has sometimes been admitted.

But now it pleads for entrance into their Homes—even into their parents' COTTAGES.

Often it will be found that a poor mother who only knows a few words of three letters, *could* learn to read such an easy book as this, with the aid of her children or of a neighbour. However small her powers, she *cannot* fail to understand these pages; and *understanding*,—she *may* feel interested,—she *may* feel encouraged. The trial has been made in numerous instances with success. An occasional visit to examine the progress of the cottager will stimulate perseverance. From the first, it should be agreed that the book must be returned, if not read. The condition will generally be performed, and the happy learner will in time put aside her baby-lessons for the HOLY SCRIPTURES. And might not a poor father do the same? And might not that father, or that mother, become the teacher of the family? And is not parents' teaching in a cottage home to be preferred even to the teaching of a Sunday School?

Happy is that village where the parents lead their little ones to the House of God, and lead them home again to read with them their little books, and—verse by verse—the Book of Books!

LESSON I

Of the Body

My dear little children;—You have seen the sun in the sky. Who put the sun in the sky?—God.

Can you reach up so high?—No.

Who holds up the sun that it does not fall?—It is God.

God lives in heaven; heaven is much higher than the sun.

Can you see God?—No.

Yet he can see you, for God sees every thing.

God made every thing at first, and God takes care of every thing. God made you, my little child, and God takes care of you always.

You have a little body; from your head down to your feet, I call your body.

Put your hand before your mouth. What do you feel coming out of your mouth? It is your breath. You breathe every moment. When you are asleep, you breathe. You cannot help breathing. But who gives you breath?

God does every thing. God gave you this little body, and he makes it live, and move, and breathe. There are bones in your body. God has made them strong and hard. There are some bones for your arms, and some bones for your legs. There is a bone for your back, and more bones for your sides.

God has covered your bones with flesh. Your flesh is soft and warm.

In your flesh there is blood. God has put skin outside, and it covers your flesh and blood like a coat.

Now all these things, the bones, and flesh, and blood, and skin, are called your body. How kind of God it was to give you a body! I hope that your body will not get hurt.

Will your bones break?—Yes, they would, if you were to fall down from a high place, or if a cart were to go over them.

If you were to be very sick, your flesh would waste away, and you would have scarcely anything left but skin and bones.

Did you ever see a child who had been sick a very long while?—I have seen a sick baby. It had not round cheeks like yours, and a fat arm like this. The baby's flesh was almost gone, and its little bones were only covered with skin. God has kept you strong and well.

LESSON IV

Of the Soul

Has God been kind to dogs? Has he given them bodies?—Yes.

Have they bones, and flesh, and blood, and skin?—Yes.

The dog has a body as well as you. Is the dog's body like yours?—No.

How many legs have you?—Two.

How many legs has the dog?—Four.

Have you got arms?—Yes, two.

Has the dog got arms?—No, it has got no arms, nor hands. But the dog has legs instead. Your skin is smooth, but the dog is covered with hair.

Is the cat's body like yours?—No; it is covered with fur.

Is a chicken's body like yours? How many legs has the chicken?—Two.

And so have you. But are its legs like yours?

His first prayer.

94

—No; the chicken has very thin, dark legs, and it has claws instead of feet.

Have you feathers on your skin? Have you wings? Is your mouth like a chicken's beak? Has the chicken any teeth?—No, the chicken's body is not at all like yours. Yet the chicken has a body—for it has flesh, and bones, and blood, and skin.

Has a fly got a body?—Yes, it has a black body, and six black legs, and two wings like glass. Its body is not at all like yours.

Who gave bodies to dogs, horses, chickens, and flies? Who keeps them alive?

God thinks of all these creatures every moment.

Can a dog thank God?—No; dogs and horses, sheep and cows cannot thank God.

Why cannot they thank God? Is it because they cannot talk?

That is not the reason.

The reason is, they cannot think of God. They never heard of God. They cannot understand about God.

Why not?—Because they have no *souls*, or spirits, like yours.

Have you got a soul?—Yes, in your body there is a soul which will never die. Your soul can think of God.

When God made your body, he put your soul inside. Are you glad of that? When God made the dogs, he put no soul like yours inside their bodies, and they cannot think of God.

Can I see your soul?—No; I cannot see it. No one can see it but God. He knows what you are thinking of now.

Which is the best, your soul or your body? —Your soul is a great deal the best. Why is your soul the best?— Your body can die, but your soul cannot die.

Shall I tell you what your body is made of? —Of dust. God made the dust into flesh and blood.

What is your soul made of?—Your soul, or spirit, is made of the breath of God.

That little dog will die some day. Its body will be thrown away. The dog will be quite gone when its body is dead. But when your body dies, your soul will be alive, and you will not be quite gone.

Where would you be put, if you were dead?— Your body would be put in a hole in the ground, but your soul would not be in the hole. Even a little baby has a soul, or a spirit.

One day as I was walking in the streets, I saw a man carrying a box. Some people were walking behind, crying.—Was the soul of the baby in the box?—No, its soul was gone up to God.

Will you not thank God for giving you a spirit? Will you not ask him to take your spirit to live with him when your body dies? Say to God, 'Pray, take my spirit to live with thee when my body dies and turns into dust.'

CHILD

Tell me, mamma, if I must die
    One day, as little baby died;
And look so very pale, and lie
    Down in the pit-hole by his side?

Shall I leave dear papa and you,
    And never see you any more?
Tell me, mamma, if this is true;
    I did not know it was before.

MAMMA

'Tis true, my love, that you must die;
    The God who made you says you must;
And every one of us shall lie,
    Like the dear baby, in the dust.

These hands, and feet, and busy head,
Shall waste and crumble right away;
But though your body shall be dead,
    There is a part which can't decay.

Jane Taylor's Hymns for Infant
Minds.

What is that part which can't decay?—It is your soul.

Your body will decay; it will turn into dust; but your soul will live for ever: it will never decay.

LESSON V

Of the Good Angels

You know that God lives in heaven. He has no body, for he is a spirit.

Does he live in heaven alone?—No; angels stand all round his throne.

What are angels?—Angels are spirits.

They are bright like the sun, but they are not so bright as God, for he is brighter than the sun. The angels are always looking at God, and it is

God that makes them shine so bright.

They sing sweet songs about God. They say. 'How good God is, how wise! how great!'

There is no night in heaven, for the angels are never tired of singing, and they never wish to sleep. They are never sick, and they will never die.

They never weep; there are no tears upon their cheeks, but sweet smiles, for angels are always happy.

If the angels were naughty, they would be unhappy. Naughtiness always makes people unhappy. The angels are quite good. They love God very much, and mind all he says.

They have wings, and can fly very quickly. God sends them down here to take care of us. As soon as God tells an angel to go, he begins to fly. They are very strong, and can keep us from harm.

Should you like the angels to be near you at night?

Do you know this pretty verse of hymn?

> I lay my body down to sleep,
>   Let angels guard my head,
> And through the hours of darkness keep
>   Their watch about my bed.

You must ask God to send the angels, for they never go, except when God sends them.

God is their Father. They have not two Fathers, as you have. The angels are the children of God, and live in God's house in heaven. When you mind what your father tells you, then you are like the angels who mind God.

The angels love us very much. They wish us to grow good, and to come to live with them in heaven. When a child is sorry for its naughtiness and prays to God to forgive it, the angels are very much pleased.

When a little child, who loves God, falls sick, and is going to die, God says to the angels, 'Go and fetch that little child's soul up to heaven.' Then the angels fly down, the little darling shuts its eyes, it lays its head on its mother's bosom, its breath stops;—the child is dead. Where is its soul? the angels are carrying it up to heaven.

How happy the child is now! Its pain is over; it is grown quite good; it is bright like an angel. It holds a harp in its hand, and begins to sing a sweet song of praise to God. Its little body is put into a grave, and turns into dust. One day God will make its body alive again.

Dear children, will you pray to God to send his angels to fetch your souls when you die?

TEMPER;

OR

THE STORY

OF

SUSAN AND BETSY.

LONDON:

Printed for

THE RELIGIOUS TRACT SOCIETY;

AND SOLD BY J. DAVIS, AT THE DEPOSITORY 56, PATERNOSTER ROW; J. NISBET, 21, BERNERS STREET, OXFORD STREET; AND OTHER BOOKSELLERS.

MISS BELL was a teacher in a Sunday school. She loved her little scholars dearly, and took great pains for their improvement. She was pleased to see them constant in their attendance at school, and diligent in their learning. She was glad when she found any quick in learning to read, and spell, and repeat. She had always something new and pleasant and instructive to teach them; and she delighted to see them understand and remember what they were taught.

But though these things pleased her much, there was something that she desired still more. She sometimes used to say to them, 'We wish that what you are taught may sink deep into your hearts, and make you better children than those who have not had your advantages, and better than you were yourselves before you knew about these things. We teach you about the Saviour, hoping that your hearts may feel gratitude and love towards him, that you may desire his favour, and endeavour to please him.'

Among her scholars were two little girls, named Susan and Betsy, concerning whom she had often felt anxious. These little girls took so much pains to improve, that they were generally at the top of their class; they could almost always not only remember the texts, but give a very pretty account of the sermons they heard. Beside this they were remarked as good children for speaking the truth, and being honest in their little dealings. Perhaps you will wonder what their fault might be: then I must inform you it was—TEMPER.

Their teacher sometimes observed with pain that the countenances of both girls bore the marks of peevishness and ill-humour; she had several times seen them teasing the little ones, or answering their questions in a pettish ill-natured way; or triumphing over those whose

places they might have taken in the class; or sullen if they happened to have lost their own; and generally quite unwilling to own themselves in a fault, and ask forgiveness. Once, in particular, they had a violent quarrel together; and were both much agitated when they came up in their class ...

When school was over, Miss Bell desired these two girls to remain, and as soon as the other children were gone, she called them to her, and spoke to them in a very serious and affectionate manner ... Miss Bell told then she had no doubt but there were faults on both sides; and as they did not appear able to give any clear account of the beginning of the quarrel, they had better bring it to a good end, by being willing on both sides to forget and forgive the past, and endeavour to be good friends for the future. Then she waited a little, but they were still sullen and stubborn. At length Miss Bell asked them; 'Children, do you ever pray?' 'Yes, ma'am,' they both replied, 'night and morning.' 'And do you wish that the great God should hear and answer your prayers?' asked the teacher. 'To be sure we do,' answered the children. 'Then kneel down and repeat the Lord's prayer.' When they came to the petition, 'And forgive us our trespasses as we'—Susan burst into tears, and said, 'Oh Betsy, do let us forgive each other, and not quarrel any more. Are you willing to be friends?' 'Yes,' said Betsy, 'we will be friends for the future.' ...

Now I must tell you that Susan laid these things to heart. The Holy Spirit of God impressed upon her mind the words of her teacher; and thus, though she had severe struggles, yet she was daily gaining victories over herself and her evil tempers. Betsy, I am sorry to say, did not act thus wisely; she never felt the sin of her perverse and evil tempers; she was never humbled before God on account of them, nor did she strive to subdue them.

These girls about the same time left school, and went to service. Betsy could never stay long in one family; for if there were fellow-servants, she never could agree with them; and if there were none, then she showed off her tempers in insolence and stubbornness towards her master and mistress, or in unkindness to the children. At last she married, and a weary life her husband led; she was so quarrelsome, passionate, and discontented, that he was soon driven to the public house, where he spent all his earnings, and left her to regret the ill temper that was the cause of all her calamities. As for Susan, conscious of her own defects, she often requested her mistress to warn and reprove her when she was wrong; and Susan lived happily in that family seven or eight years. After the death of her good mistress, she went to her daughter, where she lived until she was married. Her house is the abode of peace and content; and her husband admires her more and more as he sees her adorned with the 'ornament of a meek and quiet spirit.'

'I'm Grandmother!'

'I'm Grandfather!'

LITTLE KISSES

FOR

LITTLE MISSES

LONDON
GEORGE ROUTLEDGE AND SONS
BROADWAY, LUDGATE HILL
NEW YORK: 416 BROOME STREET

UNDER THE MISTLETOE

With a sprig of mistletoe—
  Grandmamma caught napping—
Master Dick doth softly go,
  Hand on chair-back clapping.

'Steady, steady, now's the time
  For a kiss, dear Granny;
When you wake it *will* be prime—
  I love you best of any!'

QUITE A MAN!

Little Fred is going down into the country to spend his holidays. The guard wishes to put him into a carriage with some ladies, but Fred objects to be 'taken care of.' 'Can't I have a carriage to myself, Guard?' cries he.

YOUNG LAMBS TO SELL!

Everybody knows the man who goes about crying, 'young lambs to sell!' Poor man! he has to sell a great many before he gets enough money to buy a dinner with!

GRANDPAPA

'Many happy returns of the day, Grandpapa,' says little Maud, the youngest of the group, whom the others have put forward to greet 'dear Grandpapa' on his birthday.

BUTTERCUPS AND DAISIES

Little Anne, how pleased she gazes
On her buttercups and daisies!

GRANDPAPA'S STICK

'Now then, Grandpapa, here's your stick,' cries Winnie. 'Stop, stop, little Missie,' says Grandpapa, 'you young folks are too fast for me. Let me put on my gloves first.'

WATERCRESSES

Watercresses, watercresses,
In the stream so clear and cool;
I must get you, for time presses,
Early, ere I go to school!

Tub-night.

103

HOME SWEET HOME

A RIDE WITH UNCLE

Edith has a roguish little pony with a shaggy mane, 'such a love,' she says. She delights in a canter with Uncle John, who is always ready for it.

THE NEW SHOES

A new pair of shoes.
Red or blue, Miss? pray choose.

YES, for after all 'there's no place like *Home*.' Little boys and girls run out to play. They like play. And it is quite right they should play, for it does good to their health, only they must not play on the Sabbath, or in such a way as to hurt one another. But when they have done playing, what do they think of next, why of *Home* to be sure. Their mother is there, and there when tired and hungry after playing they go, to get a good piece of bread and butter, and sit down by their own fireside, O what a nice place is *Home!*

Well, after a good wash, they put on their night-gowns, and after kneeling down at their mother's lap, and saying,

'Gentle Jesus, meek and mild,
Look upon a little child:'

or some other pretty little prayer, they go to their own warm bed, and sleep as sound as a top.

God Almighty has given them fathers and mothers, who will work for them, and take care of them, and provide for them a good basin of sweet bread and milk for breakfast, a hearty dinner of pudding, meat, and potatoes, and then some nice tea and bread and butter at night; and in the day-time send them to school, to be taught how to read and write, and behave well. Many other good things have they—good clothes, and clean linen, and warm stockings, and sound shoes, and when they are poorly, good medicine to make them better.

Who would not be thankful for such a *Home*? It is worth calling *Home*. But there are some poor little creatures who have *no Home*—no home like this—no place worth calling home. Their fathers and mothers are either very silly people or very idle. Some fathers and mothers are very poor, for want of work, or because they have been ill. Such people deserve pity and help. But look at those dirty ragged children. Their clothes are never mended; their linen all in rags, and seldom washed; their stockings are full of great holes; and their shoes, if they have any, out at the toes, or down at the heels. They have no hats or bonnets, and their hands and faces are so dirty, and their hair never combed, and their poor cold feet caked with such black dirt, that it would take a bucket of hot water, and half a pound of soap, and a scrubbing-brush to get them clean. Where do they live? Follow them to where they go, and you will soon find

that the place in which they live is as filthy almost as a stable or a pigstye. Look at the house floor, covered over with dirt. It looks as if it were never swept or washed. The walls are nearly as black as the floor, as if they were never whitewashed. They are very few things in the house—a few broken chairs and stools, and an old table, a sooty greasy tin kettle, and a few pots; and if you went up stairs you would see such a chamber!—the bed made of straw, and a few old rugs or sacks to cover them, and there they lie, all huddled together, like so many pigs in a stye. This is true: quite true of many. And why is it so? It is almost always because of one thing—and that is *drunkenness*. The father spends his money in beer or ale, which he ought to bring home for his wife to spend in buying bread and milk, and meat, to feed the children, and with which she could get some furniture, and other things, which she wants to make the house comfortable. But sometimes, which is worse than all, the mother is a drunkard too, and loves gin; and if she does, there is sure to be no good; for she will go to the pawn shop till she has sold every bit of furniture in the house, and

even her very clothes off her back, but she will have that nasty gin.

This is the way that poor, ragged, dirty, half-starved children are made. O how would you like to have such a home as theirs? See, then, what a good thing it is to have a good home. You can never be too thankful to God, and too thankful to your parents for such a home.

LITTLE MARY'S PICTURE RIDDLES

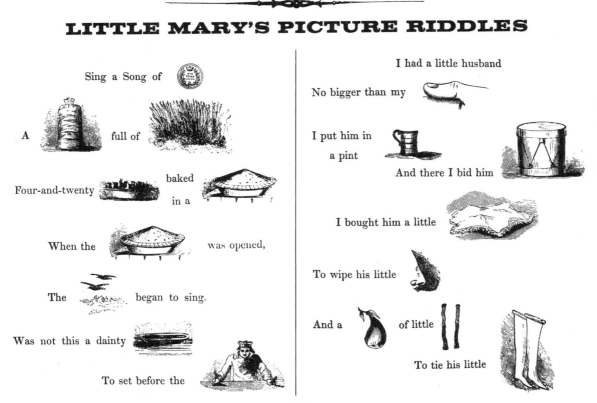

The was in his counting-house,

Counting out his

The was in the

Eating and

The was in the garden,

hanging out the

There came a little and pecked off her

Hush-a-bye on the

When the wind blows, the will

When the breaks,

The will fall.

Down will come cradle, and all.

go fore with and

And I'll follow after on little Jack

Great A little a bouncing

The 's in the

And she can't

Anne, Anne, sit in the

As fair as a as white as a

I send you so pray read

must read if you can't read

And so, Miss or Master, throw up the

108

LITTLE MITES FOR TINY SPRITES

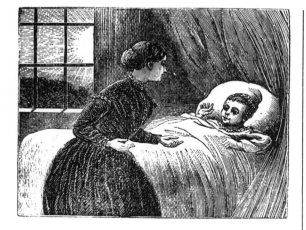

BABY CHARLIE

Baby, baby Charlie,
    Naughty in his play,
Slapping little Annie,
    Pushing her away!

Kiss the baby, darling,
    Kiss the little one;
He is only playing,
    In his baby fun.

MORNING

Awake, little girl, it is time to arise,
    Come, shake drowsy sleep from your eye;
The lark is now warbling his notes to the skies,
    And the sun is far mounted on high.

Oh, come, for the fields with gay flowers abound,
    The dewdrop is quivering still,
The lowing herds graze in the pastures around,
    And the sheep-bell is heard from the hill.

THE LITTLE CRIPPLE

I'm a helpless cripple child,
    Gentle Christians, pity me;
Once in rosy health I smiled,
    Blithe and gay as you can be,
And upon the village green
First in every sport was seen.

Let not then the scoffing eye
    Laugh, my twisted leg to see:
Gentle Christians, passing by,
    Stop awhile, and pity me;
And for you I'll breathe a prayer;
Leaning in my easy chair.

OLD AGE

Who is this that comes tottering along?
   His footsteps are feeble and slow,
His beard has grown curling and long,
   And his hair is turn'd white as the snow.

Little stranger, his name is Old Age,
   His journey will shortly be o'er:
He soon will leave life's busy stage,
   To sigh and be sorry no more.

THE BLIND SAILOR

A sailor, with a wooden leg,
   A little charity implores;
He holds his tatter'd hat to beg,—
   Come let us join our little stores.
Poor sailor! we ourselves might be
As helpless and as poor as he.

'A thousand thanks, my lady kind,
   A thousand blessings on your head;
A flash of lightning struck me blind,
   Or else I would not beg my bread.
I pray that you may never be
A poor blind wanderer like me.'

GOING TO BED

Receive my body, pretty bed;
Soft pillow, oh, receive my head;
   And thanks, my parents kind,
For comforts you for me provide;
Your precepts still shall be my guide,
   Your love I'll keep in mind.

Waiting for the train.

MEMOIRS OF A LONDON DOLL

Chapter X

PLAYING WITH FIRE

A message was sent to a celebrated milliner in Piccadilly to come immediately and take orders for ball dresses, for Lady Flora and her doll.

At last the dresses came home. They were beautiful, and both exactly alike. They were made of the thinnest white gauze, to be worn over very full petticoats of the same white gauze; so that they set out very much, and looked very soft and fleecy. They were trimmed with an imitation of lily of the valley, made in white satin and silver. The trowsers were of white satin, trimmed with gauze.

The day of the ball was rather cold and windy; so that, although it was the month of August, a fire was ordered in the nursery, and in Lady Flora's bed-room, lest she might take cold. Towards evening the dresses were all laid out ready to put on; but when my mamma saw them, she could not wait, and insisted on being dressed, although it was five hours before the time. In two hours and a half she was ready; and then I was dressed, which occupied an hour more. Still there was a long time to wait; so Lady Flora took me in her arms, and began to dance from room to room,—that is, from the nursery to her bed-room, from one fire-place to the other. In doing this, she observed that each time she turned, her full, gauze frock gave the fire a *puff*, so that a blaze came; and as she was amused by it, she went each time nearer, and whisked round quicker in order to make the blaze greater. 'Oh, Lady Flora!' cried her maid, 'pray take care of your dress; you go too near; wait till I run and fetch the fire-guards.'

Away ran the maid to fetch the fire-guards; and while she was gone Lady Flora determined to dance for the last time still nearer than ever to each fire before she whisked round. The very next time she did it she went just the least bit too near; the hem of her frock whisked against the bars—and her frock was in a blaze in a moment!

She gave a loud scream and a jump, and was going to run, when most fortunately her foot caught one corner of a thick rug, and down she fell. This smothered the blaze, but still her clothes were on fire; and she lay shrieking and rolling and writhing on the floor.

Up ran the nursery maid, and when she saw what had happened, she began screaming too—and up ran the very tall footman, and the instant he looked into the room, and smelt the fire, he ran away again as fast as possible—and then up ran the countess herself, and she ran straight to her child, and rolled the thick rug round her, and carried her in her arms to her own room.

Physicians and surgeons were sent for, and all the burnt things were taken off, and thrown on one side. Among these I lay; my beautiful dress was all black tinder; but I was not really much burnt, nor was Lady Flora. A few weeks might cure her, though the scars would always remain, and spoil her prettiness; but what could cure *me*? I was so scorched and frizzled, that the paint which was on my skin had blistered and peeled off. I was quite black. No notice was

115

taken of me; and in the confusion I was carried out of the room, with the rest of the burnt rags, and thrown by one of the servants, in her haste, out of a back window.

How I escaped utter destruction, in this dreadful fall, I cannot think; unless it was owing to my being wrapped all round in singed clothes, so that I fell softly. I had nearly fainted with fear, when the flames first caught my dress; and when the housemaid threw open the window to fling me out, my senses utterly forsook me.

I fell over a low wall, into a passage leading towards some stables. In the course of a few minutes I recovered my senses, but only to experience a fresh alarm! A fine large Newfoundland dog, who was just passing, thought somebody had thrown him a broiled bone; so he caught me up in his mouth, and away he ran with me, wagging his tail.

THE BAND OF THE RED, WHITE AND BLUE

There waves the Flag of England,
  The old 'Red, White and Blue!'
Play up, my gallant Drummer,
  A loud, rat-tat-a-too,
As we go marching onward
  In all our brave array,
On to the field of battle,
  To conquer, not to slay.
Look at our Sergeant Maggie,
  How boldly she steps out!
Were she to meet a foeman
  She'd send him 'right about.'
And as for Private Johnnie,
  Our noble Grenadier,
He's every inch a soldier—
  Don't talk to *him* of fear.
Play up again, brave Drummer!
  My noble Army, whistle!
We're fighting for the Shamrock,
  The Roses and the Thistle:
We're fighting for the children
  Who pine in rags for bread;
We're fighting for the pennies
  To get them clothed and fed.
We're fighting for the children
  Who have no homes like ours,
Who never see the sunshine,
  And never smell the flowers.
'Rat-tat-a-too, rat-tat-a-too,'
  All who have pennies, give them, do!

'DRIVE TO BETHNAL GREEN'

ONE DAY, just as a beautiful young Duchess had go into her carriage, and the footman was waiting to know where she wished to be driven, a poor little beggar girl came up, and entreated for help, saying that her mother was ill, and that she and her little brothers and sisters were starving for want of bread. There was something in the child's manner that touched the heart of the Duchess, and instead of carelessly giving her a shilling, she directed her coachman to drive to the wretched alley at Bethnal Green where the child lived, saying she would go herself and see the child's mother, and inquire into the truth of her story. So, greatly to the splendid footman's disgust, the carriage drove to Bethnal Green instead of to the Park, and the kind Duchess did all she could for the poor family she found there, and was rewarded by feeling that she had been useful as well as beautiful for once in her life.

In a pretty *datcha* or country house some twenty miles away from St Petersburg, lived an English family consisting of a gentleman and his wife and two little daughters. In the winter time they resided in the city, but, like most people who could afford a change, they always went away to the country for the summer months.

One morning, when the Russian nurse came into the children's room to help them in dressing, the little girls noticed that she had been crying very much. Her poor old eyes were swollen, and her cheeks were quite pale.

'Oh, *Niania*' (nurse) 'what is the matter?' cried both children in a breath.

'Why have you been crying?'

Poor nurse began to sob again.

'Ah, my dear little ladies,' she said, 'my sister who lives not far from here has just been taken ill; so ill, that perhaps she will not get well any more. You know, dear children, she is a widow and has a little boy and girl, and she has worked for them for years, and with the help I could manage to give them they have got on somehow. But now I do not know what is to become of them.'

'I am sure mamma will do something for them,' said Ella, the eldest girl.

'And can't we do something too?' cried little May, a bright, sunny-faced darling, and the pet of all.

Ella thought for a moment or two silently, then she said,

'Nurse, don't your little niece and nephew go about selling mushrooms sometimes?'

'Yes, my dear, they do,' replied nurse, 'for all the gentry like them; and sometimes the children make money enough in the autumn by their mushrooms to buy them each a cap, or hood, or pair of boots.'

'And if they could get twice as many mushrooms, I suppose they would have twice as much money,' resumed Ella thoughtfully.

'Yes, without doubt, *Galoubashka*' (which means 'little dove').

'Then, May dear, this is what we will do,' said Ella. 'Instead of gathering mushrooms in the woods every day just for our own eating, let us give all we find to Pashinka, and Colia to sell, and then we too shall be doing something to help them in their trouble.'

'But it will be hard for you, my dears, to do without the mushrooms that you have for din-

ner every day, and which I know you like so much,' said nurse.'

'Yes, but mamma says that in every true giving there is some self-denial,' rejoined Ella. 'And it will be a pleasure for May and me to give up something, won't it, May?'

The very next morning the children set out on a mushroom hunt. They went farther than usual and never had they been so successful, for they brought home two large basketsful of various kinds.

Every child in Russia is brought up to know the good mushrooms from the bad, and you never hear of any one being poisoned, although a number of varieties are eaten which either in England or in France are considered toadstools.

So Ella and May went without their daily treat throughout the mushroom season, and gave all that they found to the little Russians to sell; and with this help and some assistance from Ella's and May's mother, the rent of the little house was paid, food and medicine were bought, and at last the children had the satisfaction of seeing that nurse's sister was really getting well again, Indeed, by the time the mushroom season was over, she was able to

work once more as she had done before, and all anxiety was at an end.

Ah, little friends, you see that even children can do something for others, and through others for their dear Master and Saviour.

If you are but willing to exercise a little self-denial for His sake, there is much that you can do. Try it in your every-day life, and see if the happiness and peace that come to you, do not more than make up for the little things which you deny yourselves. And remember for your encouragement who has said, 'For as much as ye did it unto one of the least of these My brethren, ye did unto Me.'

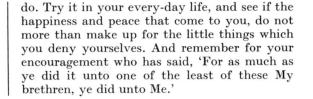

HOPE AFTER DESPAIR

VERY often application is made for the admission to the Homes of very poor children who are not orphans nor really distitute. They have a father and a mother, but the father has left them—perhaps for a year, or two years, or three years even. Nobody knows where he is, and the poor mother has done her best to maintain the children, but is at length brought to a starving condition.

There is nothing then for her but the workhouse, and sometimes these poor creatures will rather even starve than enter the 'Union,' as the workhouse is called. And so they come to me and ask me to help them, by taking perhaps one or two children out of the many that form the family, and thus relieve her for a while of her pressing burden. It is with great grief that I frequently find myself unable to help such cases; because of course it would never do, as my little readers may imagine, to take in children whose fathers are alive and OUGHT to support their families. This reminds me of a story, which although very sad at the beginning had a brighter end:—

A poor woman made application for the admission of her little girl. She lived with her two children in a poor garret near; it had almost no furniture,—scarcely an article except one or two stools, and a table lent by a neighbour. But a city missionary had found them out, and besides other occasional help had given them three or four flower-pots; and these were greatly prized by the little girl, who put them in the window and watched over them day after day. The mother was a tailoress; she worked very hard for herself, her little girl, and a little baby-boy nineteen months old. Her husband had left her more than a year ago, she said, to get work in some other part, but she had never heard from him since then, and she was reduced almost to starvation.

One day—it was a bright winter's day—they had had nothing to eat for nearly twenty-four hours; they had not paid their rent for a month, and were every day expecting that the landlord would turn them out into the street, when a man's footstep was heard upon the stair—a steady tramp, tramp. The poor mother had fallen asleep utterly exhausted with famine and fatigue, with the baby in her lap, when the door opened, and a strong, well-clad, industrious-looking working-man entered the room. Without a word, fearing to awake her mother, little Emily went to him and threw her arms around him, and said in such a gentle tone, 'Oh, father, I am so glad you have come back!'

Yes, it *was* her father; and he stood gazing at his poor wife, so pale and thin and wan, who, asleep sitting on a low stool, looked almost as if she were dead; and he felt himself unable to restrain his tears. You may imagine what a bright, happy awaking it was when this poor woman found her husband had come back, and how sorry he was to learn of her distress.

It seems he had written two or three times, and even sent her money; but she had never had the letters, and supposed her husband had forgotten her; whereas he imagined that the money he had sent had helped to support his wife, and that the letters had given her courage and contentment. Our picture will help you to understand what the scene was like; but you can never see the joy that shone on little Emily's face when next week she came round to me quite nicely clad and looking peaceful and happy, as she said, 'Oh, sir, I don't want to come into the Home *now*, thank you! Father has come home!'

Alas! for thousands of poor children who have not such a father; whose poor mother is dead or unable to assist them; and who wander about the streets, homeless, friendless, and destitute! For them our doors are always open.

LIVELY LAYS FOR DREARY DAYS

CAUGHT BY THE TIDE

Fred, in alarm, flings down his net,
And catches Flo (his darling pet),
    And in his arms he holds her tight.
'Grasp my jacket, May!' he cries,
As to gain the shore he tries,
    And struggles on with all his might.

—

THE SAND CASTLE

The tide is out, and all the strand
    Is glistening in the summer sun;
Let's build a castle of the sand—
    Oh! will not that be glorious fun?

With walls and outworks wide and steep,
    All round about we'll dig a moat,
And in the midst shall be the keep
    Where our old flag may proudly float.

GIRLS' PLAY

I, and little May, and Jane,
    Are so happy with our flowers.
Jane is culling foxglove bells,
    May and I are making posies,
And we want to search the dells
    For the latest summer roses.

'Come with me!'

Afraid to go home.

126

th us
tr acc
tr act
tr ail
tr ait[70]
tr eat
tr ice
tr ope
tr out
tw ice
tw ill
wh ale

Whale.

wh all
wh at[21]
wh eat
wh eel
wh elk
wh elm
wh ere
wh it
wh ort
wr apt
wr it
wr its

SPELLING XIII.

Affix of two letters to a word in Part I. See Note 89.

on ce
dan ce
far ce
fen ce
for ce
hen ce
Nan ce
pea ce
pen ce
pie ce[37]
sin ce
spa ce
win ce

See how the doll can dance!

127

Water-spout.

Goldfish.

headlong	godchild
holdfast	goddaughter
goldfish	godfather
godson	godmother
God-speed	greyhound
Godward	greenhouse

fire-place	handrail
arm-chair	water-spout
privy-seal	chairman
hearth-rug	headache
fireside	mousetrap
handbook	landlord
handcuff	handmaid

Farmhouse.—Carthorse.

**Fire-place.—Arm-chair.—
Hearth-rug.**

mother-wit	trueblue
newspaper	truebred
farmhouse	truehearted
carthouse	truelove
staircase	waistcoat
stockdove	water-man
thunderbolt	water-mark
to-night	ash-pit

Is this the right key?

IX.	by	climb *	site*	size
I	bye	clime	sight	sise
ay	buy	I'll	cite	sighs
aye*	hie	isle	slight	quire*
eye	high	aisle	sleight	choir

SECTION III.—*Words compounded of Greek and Latin Root-words.*

SPELLING XCII.

monarchy .	189, 83
protomartyr	190, 106
deuteronomy	191, 48
triglyphic .	192, 28
tetrarchate	193, 83
pentagraph .	194, 154
pentateuch .	194, 141
hexameter .	195, 150
heptarchy .	196, 83
octagon . .	197, 142
enneagon .	198, 142
decalogue .	199, 161
barometer .	484, 150
necropolis .	111, 188
metropolis .	498, 188
necromancy	498, 105
oxygen . .	496, 486
oxygon . .	496, 142
astrolatry .	6, 495
demonolatry	93, 495
cosmolatry .	20, 495
heliolatry .	145, 495
pyrolatry .	133, 495
eucharist .	97, 497
spheroid .	499, 490
homonym .	491, 117
onomancy .	117, 105

The thermometer.

pyromancy.	133, 105	eupathy .	97, 123	euphonism .	57, 98
rabdomancy	144, 105	isothermal .	493, 488	evangelist* .	97, 185
oneiromancy	116, 105	isochronal .	493, 17	baroscope .	484, 487
lithomancy.	42, 105	logomachy .	161, 494	microscope .	46, 487
philosopher	126, 450	psychomachy	132, 494	stereoscopic .	70, 487
theosophy .	137, 450	sciomachy .	65, 494	telescope . .	72, 487
uranoscope .	55, 487	cardialgia .	158, 485	astronomy .	6, 48
hieroglyphic	33, 28	neuralgia .	115, 485	thermometer.	488, 150
heliotrope .	145, 492	odontalgia .	53, 485	geometry .	26, 150

* *Ev* for *eu*.

No. 76. June 10th, 1876.

WEEKLY. { CHEAP EDITION, ONE HALFPENNY
DRAWING-ROOM EDITION, 1d.

THE CHILDREN'S TREASURY
AND ADVOCATE OF
THE HOMELESS AND DESTITUTE
CONDUCTED BY
DR BARNARDO
OF THE EAST END JUVENILE MISSION

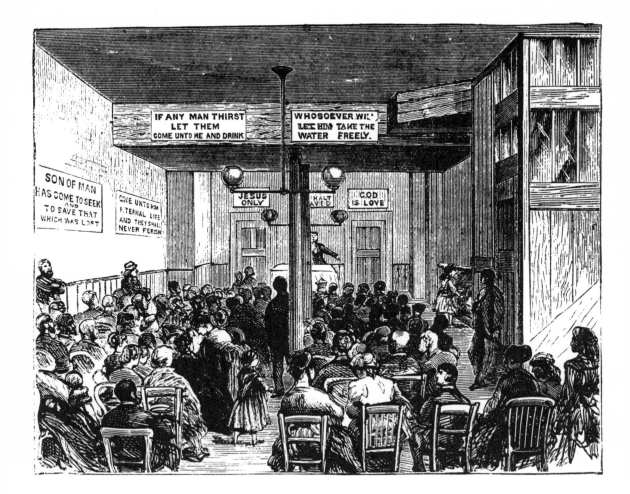

MERCY'S HOUSE

In the midst of a very poor and squalid part of East London, there is a dear little building, which stands like a lighthouse, shedding bright beams on the darkness and misery around. It is called 'The Medical Mission', and as I have explained before, poor people who are sick come to that house, in which are two kind doctors who endeavour to discover what is the matter, and who prescribe proper medicines for them. Then there are several gentle ladies who make up the medicines that the doctors prescribe— who dress the wounds of the poor people, and who speak kind, loving words to them, and afterwards visit them at their homes, and so endeavour to lead them to the GREAT PHYSICIAN, who can heal *the soul* as well as the body.

Would you like to take a peep into the Medical

132

Mission? You cannot see the patients while they come in one by one into the doctor's little consulting room, for *that* is quite a private room; but we can let you look into the waiting hall, where they sit until their turn comes to be spoken to privately; and if you look at our picture, you will notice that one of the doctors is speaking to them from a little raised platform at the end of the hall. By-and-by some kind ladies will sing sweet hymns, which will cheer and comfort the poor sick folk, and then, as they go away, a little bunch of flowers will perhaps be given to each one; that is, if our friends in the country have thought of us, and have sent us, as they sometimes do, a supply.

I hope my young friends will some day be able to visit and see for themselves the various interesting works described in these pages.

MRS HILTON'S CRÈCHE

COME with me into this pleasant room. What a happy, busy scene! What numbers of little children are happily amusing themselves. This is Mrs Hilton's Crèche.

This good lady was distressed to see little children tumbling about the streets, exposed to all sorts of accidents and dangers, while their mothers were away earning the daily bread. So she determined to care for them. She opened a home where poor mothers, for a very small sum, could leave their little children all day quite safely. Kind nurses are provided to look after the little ones, and good food is also given, while there are most inviting little cots, where the tinies can have a peaceful midday rest.

There are toys of all sorts, and bright flowers in the windows, while texts from God's own Word are placed round the walls. Everything is beautifully fresh and clean, and must be a great contrast to many of the homes of the poor children. No wonder they like to come to the pleasant, cheerful rooms of the Crèche, and play about there, without any fear of blows or hard words, such as they often got in the streets.

But besides these day-children, Mrs Hilton also takes in orphans, and keeps them altogether, nursing them and caring for them, and making their childhood happier than their parents ever dreamed. Is it not a blessed work? Will you not ask mamma or auntie to take you down to see this happy little band on your next holiday? Then you will see for yourselves how bright it all is.

THE ORPHAN BOY

'Stay, lady, stay, for mercy's sake,
  And hear a helpless orphan's tale;
Ah! sure my looks must pity wake,
  'Tis want that makes my cheeks so pale!

'Yet I was once a mother's pride,
  And my brave father's hope and joy;
But in the Nile's proud fight he died,
  And I am now an orphan boy.

'Poor foolish child—how pleased was I,
  When news of Nelson's victory came;
Along the crowded streets to fly,
  And see the lighted windows flame!

'To force me home my mother sought,
  She could not bear to see my joy;
For with my father's life 'twas bought,
  And made me a poor orphan boy!

'The people's shouts were long and loud,
  My mother, shuddering, closed her ears;
"Rejoice! rejoice!" still cried the crowd,
  My mother answered with her tears.

'"Why are you crying thus," said I,
  While others laugh and shout with joy?'
She kissed me, and with such a sigh
  She called me her poor orphan boy.

'"What is an orphan boy?" I said,
  When suddenly she gasped for breath,
And her eyes closed—I shrieked for aid,
  But, ah! her eyes were closed in death.

'My hardships since I will not tell!
  But now no more a parent's joy:
Ah! lady, I have learned too well
  What 'tis to be an orphan boy!

'Oh! were I by your bounty fed—
  Nay, gentle lady, do not chide;
Trust me—I mean to earn my bread,
  The sailor's orphan boy has pride.

'Lady! you weep—ah! this to me!
  You'll give me clothing, food, employ!
Look down, dear parents, look and see
  Your happy—happy orphan boy!'

Amelia Opie.

'OUR MERCIFUL BRIGADE;'
or,
THE CHILDREN'S HUMANE SOCIETY

Our Merciful Brigade.

PLEDGE.

"I AGREE TO DO ALL IN MY POWER TO BE KIND TO EVERY CREA-
TURE WHOM GOD HAS MADE; TO PROTECT ANIMALS FROM CRUEL
USAGE; TO PROMOTE ALSO, AS FAR AS I CAN, THEIR HUMANE TREAT-
MENT; NEVER TO ROB OR DESTROY A BIRD'S NEST; AND TO ENDEA-
VOUR TO GET AS MANY BOYS AND GIRLS AS POSSIBLE TO BECOME
MEMBERS OF

"Our Merciful Brigade."

Signed ....

Age last Birthday ....

Residence ....

Date ....

"Blessed are the merciful, for they shall obtain mercy."

If every young reader into whose hands these pages come will read carefully the following pledge, and then, with the consent of father or mother, or teacher, or guardian, write it out fully on a piece of paper, and sign below their own name, age, address, and the date, and send the same, with twopence in postage stamps, to 'UNCLE TOM,' 18, Stepney Causeway, London, E., he will register their names as members of 'Our Merciful Brigade,' and send them each a beautiful little card of membership, which may be framed and hung up in the member's bed-room.

VISITING THE POOR

THERE are many persons who live in large houses and have plenty of money, who have little thought for the poor around them. They so seldom go among their poor neighbours that they seem scarcely to be aware of how they live, or what they need. This is not right, for it does us good to call and see those who are poor or sick. Even if we have nothing to give them, we can speak kindly to them, and show by our manner that we take an interest in them. Mrs Price is a kind lady, who often calls on the poor around her, and this morning she has brought her little son and daughter with her. The poor woman, with her bare room, her ragged clothes, and her sick child, is very glad to see a kind face and a helping hand at her door, for she is in trouble and distress, and has just been wondering how she could give the hungry children anything to eat. The Bible teaches us, in many places, to remember the poor, and we should never forget to do them good, especially if God sends us plenty for ourselves.

DREAMS

If children have been good all day,
    And kept their tongues and lips quite clean,
They dream of flowers that nod and play,
    And fairies dancing on the green.

But if they've spoken naughty words,
    Or told a lie, they dream of rats:
Of crawling snakes, and ugly birds;
    Of centipedes, and vampire bats.

❦

THE DANGER OF THE STREETS

'PERHAPS become a thief!' I wrote in last week's number, when describing the evils to which poor street children were exposed.

I dare say some of my young readers shuddered to think of any poor boy or girl being *compelled* to do what is wrong—forced into evil by the trials of their lot; yet I only state a well-known fact, when I say that very many *are* tempted to act wickedly every day in London, and because they have no one to tell them it is wrong or to help them to do right, they fall into sinful ways, and become habitually wicked.

Let me tell you the story of two children whom I once helped, and who had been sorely tempted, but whom the Lord graciously preserved. Theirs was a very interesting case. They lived with their mother, Mrs Sewell, in a very poor and narrow street in the centre of London. She was very ill for a long time, and her son whose name was Henry, came to his wit's end in trying to obtain the necessaries of life for his poor mother.

He and little Emma, his only sister, often went out into the streets and begged of passers by; sometimes, however, they were driven away with unkind words or threats of the policeman. Indeed, they must all have starved but that Mrs Sewell sent Henry to pawn or sell almost everything in the wretched room where they lived that could be parted with. First the poor table and old chairs, and then two or three articles of crockery, and a picture or two, were sold one by one. At length their very clothes went. Every article the widow could spare was pawned, and even Henry's jacket had to be sold

to fetch a few pence, but with all this the children could scarcely keep life within them, or obtain what was needed for their poor dying mother.

One day they had wandered hungry and tired through some of the poorer streets near to where they lived,—they had not broken their fast that day. Imagine how wretched they felt. They had no money, and nothing to bring home to their poor mother. Henry was in despair. Presently they came to a confectioner's shop. With what hungry and longing eyes they looked at the delicacies displayed within the window!

While gazing within, Henry felt a strong hand laid upon his shoulder, and turning round, saw a man who had been standing close to them and had overheard their whispered wishes for food and help. Having observed their wretched condition, this man in a few cunning words invited Henry and Emma to come to where he lived, promising to give them food and money, and to show Henry how he could always have as much as he wished for.

The boy, who was a very nice-looking child, disliked the man's appearance, and glanced quickly at his questioner, while his large eyes had a frightened look as he said, 'It isn't to do nothing wrong, is it?'

With a grim smile upon his rough face, his tempter replied, 'Oh! if you're so nice as all that, and so pertickler, p'raps you'd better go home and starve; but if I were you, I'd rather have good food any day than go without, eh!'

'I would rather starve,' said Henry, while a quick flush came over his pale face, 'than steal, and so would mother,' and then taking Emma's hand, he turned quickly from his tempter in the direction of their wretched home, followed by the mocking laugh of the man who had accosted them.

On the staircase the children came in contact with a decently-dressed man, who was going to the top of the house, and they had hardly reached the attic where their mother lay, when the visitor arrived with slower steps on the same landing, and asked them in a kind voice if they knew if Mrs Sewell lived there.

'Oh, that's mother,' said Henry, and he brought him in.

The visitor was the Scripture Reader of the district. He had only just heard of the distress in which the children and their mother were living.

Providentially he arrived just at the right

time. He and Mrs Sewell listened with gratitude to Henry's story of his escape from temptation, and the missionary promised the poor woman, whose immediate wants he relieved, but who was fast approaching her end, that he would save the children from the streets, and take them to some Home, where they might be reared in honest and Christian ways.

When he departed, my young readers may imagine the joy he left behind him, which was increased when, in the evening, they found a basket had been sent from some kind friend, through the missionary, containing many things that they urgently needed.

'I don't smoke, my boy,' said the Gentleman.

140

Kindness to the poor.

A STREET FLOWER-GIRL

How refreshing it is as we hurry along the busy London streets to come to such a flower-girl as we have in the picture! The whiff of violets, wall-flowers, moss-rosebuds, or sweet-brier, takes us far away from the noise and bustle; and with those wonderful minds of ours we seem to see for a minute banks and lanes, cottage gardens and village children, and the peaceful scenes of country life.

'What does she ask for her flowers?'

'Only a penny a bunch!'

One may well say 'only', for it has given her real honest labour to get that glowing basket ready for her customers.

'Labour to get flowers!' You think that is nonsense, and that flowers and pleasure must go hand in hand; but wait a minute. God's law for us all is, that we must work in some way or other, and our flower-girl knows this quite as well as many of her elders.

Long before you were awake she was astir, and off from the small dark kitchen which is 'home' to her, for it holds father and mother, and Tommy and Jack, and baby, and away along the silent streets to Covent Garden Market. Early in the year *you* would still think it night, but it is morning to her, and sleepy or not, fine or wet, forth she must go, for it is the earliest comer who makes the best bargain and gets the pick of the bright bunches. She has had much to learn so as to carry on her trade success-fully—how to buy, how to arrange, how to sell her flowers; while you boys and girls have only to think whether you can find a penny or two to buy her pretty wares.

As she hurries along the streets her busy head is thinking how far her small sum of money will go, what flowers will be coming in and what chances she has of making as much or more than she did yesterday; and she forgets to notice how quiet and grand the streets look, or how the cold grey dawn is getting warm and golden with the rays of the coming sun, or how the sky is becoming tinged with the colours of dawn, softest green and blue, rosy red and gold.

The thrush in that cage she is passing sees it if she does not, and by his outburst of song al-most tempts her to stop and listen to him. But hurrying steps behind her remind her that stopping about will not fill her basket, or get her a first pick in the market. Life and stir have been growing with every step the flower-girl has taken since she left home, and now she is in the midst of a great bustle, as if it were mid-day in-stead of early, very early, morning. Waggons toppling over with cabbages, horses, hucksters' barrows, carts with men in smock-frocks press-ing forward to land their round baskets of creamy broccoli, blue-green marrowfat peas, and yellow kidney patotoes. Cherries, straw-berries, gooseberries, all are there in abundance; but our flower-girl scarcely notices them; they are daily sights to her, and her business lies out yonder among the flowers.

What a bustle and hubbub it is! Country-women fresh and blooming, town girls pale and eager, all talking, and laughing, and bargaining. The only silent things are the flowers, but how beautiful they are! and where can they all have come from? White, crimson, yellow, blue, all 'a-glowing and a-blowing,' all dewy and fresh, all sweet and pure, all ready for their day's work to give pleasure and happiness. Sharp bargaining is going on, and each is trying to do his or her best for themselves, and from the fray some come forth grumbling and discontented, and some smiling and well pleased.

This is the first step in our flower-girl's day's business; and now comes her second, which is to arrange her goods, and for this she retires be-neath the arcading which surrounds the market, and there is busy some time, making up her penny bunches and putting the larger ones in tempting array, hoping they may be purchased for tables or vases. If times have been favour-able, she has her penny for the coffee-stall, and if not—and this, alas! is too often the case—she must go without breakfast. She takes the third step in her day's proceedings when most girls and boys are leaving their warm beds, or sitting at their comfortable breakfast-tables. Then, with her basket arranged as attractively as possible, she starts for her long day's sale. Happy for her if she has a recognised stand at some busy centre, such as Oxford Circus, the Mansion House, or one of the Metropolitan Stations, where she has a brisker sale than among her private customers, of which she has some few, according to the days in the week. There is the kind, grey-headed, old gentleman with the gaiters, who always buys three-penny-worth on Friday, for 'my little maid at home' as he tells her; the cook at the corner of Garden Square, who always has a bunch to stand in a blue jug in her bright, clean kitchen window;

and the little golden-haired lady, who watches for the poor flower-girl from her nursery window, and has the basket sent in by a tall footman to pick and choose from. She always smiles and nods, and generally has her doll or some toy to hold up for 'the flower-girl to see.'

But the happiest time for our flower-girl is when, with an empty basket and her earnings safely tied in the corner of her shawl, she finds herself once more at home in the back-kitchen. Tired! Of course she is! but who thinks of such things when they are by themselves, talking over with 'mother' the day's earnings, and, when times are good, having a cup of hot tea?

JOAN was not like the rest of her little brothers and sisters, who were all strong, healthy children, who could thoroughly enjoy themselves out of doors and indoors, too, tumbling about and racing over the grass when in the garden, or swinging, or playing at any and all the boisterous, merry games that healthy children so much delight in. But Joan was different from all of these. She, poor little woman, had never been a strong child, and when the others were flying here and there out in the glad sunshine, enjoying the delightful excitement of quick motion and the sweet scents, sights and sounds of out-door life in the country, poor Joan would have to sit indoors or lie on the sofa to ease the pain in her little weak back, and only stir out of doors if the wind was in a mild quarter and the ground was dry.

Her home was far in the country, at a long distance even from the county town, and the nearest doctor lived more than seven miles away. The doctor had often said what a pity it was that she could not have the benefit of a certain great doctor's opinion, who was so clever about children, but who lived in London.

'Sir Peter Robson would be the best man to consult, depend upon it,' said Dr. Jonson. 'I should take her to town.'

And father and mother were just discussing how this was to be done, when a letter arrived from grandmamma, whose house was in London, proposing that Joan should go to her for a long visit.

At first the little girl took it very sadly, and, crying, declared she could not leave her home. 'And there is one sweet white duck that knows me *so well*; and when Wilkins wheeled me down to the pond to-day, she came waddling out of the water, so tame and kind, and looking so lovely, and quacked at me to tell me she knew me. Oh, dear, oh dear!' cried Joan, breathless and miserable, 'and I shall go away and not see her any more!'

Mother sighed, and looked very distressed, as she answered, 'I am afraid, Joan darling, that there would be no place to keep the white duck in grandmamma's house in London.'

And so Joan had to give up the idea of taking her dear white duck with her. The last morning was a very sad one to the little girl. However, the farewells were said, and soon papa, mamma, and their little invalid daughter were whirling away to London in an express train.

Grandmamma welcomed them all most affectionately, but although grandmamma dearly loved her little grandchild, and was most anxious to make her happy while she stayed with her, she was a very neat, tidy, and precise old lady.

'I cannot have a duck in the house, Joan, dear,' said her grandmother. 'Don't you think you can be made happy by a pretty doll?'

'Oh, no, grandmother,' answered Joan, 'that would not be at all the same thing.'

The next afternoon grandmamma took Joan out in the carriage, and they stopped at a splendid toy-shop. Grandmamma and her little companion were soon examining the toys together with the deepest interest, and Joan was both surprised and delighted at all the lovely things she saw. But she looked at and admired one after the other, turning away rapidly from each in a way that showed she had not set her heart on any one in particular. At last her grandmother called her to the other side of the shop. Joan ran to her side, and then granny pointed out to her a beautiful white duck, that looked exactly like a real one, for it had real plumage, the feathers just lying sofy and glossy like those really growing on Daffy-down-dilly's back. It had a yellow beak, black eyes, and two awkward-looking splay feet that might have been mistaken for the very ones Joan had so often watched waddling up to her invalid chair. And when the mistress of the shop put the creature on the ground, and turned an invisible handle in its side, it began to lift its splay feet, and walk, and flap its wings, and quack. Joan clapped her hands with joy, and exclaimed, 'My Daffy-down-dilly!'

'Now, Joan, darling,' said grandmother, 'if you will promise me to be a happy, contented little girl, you shall take this Daffy-down-dilly home with you.' And little Joan, in all truth and honesty, promised she would.

So Daffy-down-dilly was conveyed home, and was wound up many times that night before Joan went to bed. But the days passed, and somehow the toy duck did not bring the same happiness to Joan that her old real Daffy-down-dilly had done, and, although the little girl did all she could to be contented and keep her promise to her grandmother, she felt in her own little

heart that the sham thing was a terrible disappointment to her, and one day when her grandmother went into her bedroom, out of which Joan's opened, the old lady heard the child softly crying and talking to herself.

Grandmother's heart was touched. 'The child is pining for something real to pet and love,' said she, 'and that can love her in return, and she shall have it.'

So she unselfishly cast her own prejudices to the winds; and the next morning, when Joan went to the basket which she had turned into a nest for her sham Daffy-down-dilly, she found, instead of a cold, toy duck, a little, soft, warm mass of curly white hair belonging to a dear little doggie that her granny had bought for her. She took it to her heart and loved it, and named it Dilly, and the little creature returned her affection with interest. And you will be glad to hear that before many months were over Joan was home again, and she and Dilly were running races on the great lawn with 'the others'.

THE LITTLE TRACT GIRL

WHO is that little girl I see every Sunday morning pass my house? She carries in her hand a small bundle of books: what can they be about? If I meet her in an hour's time, there are not so many in the parcel as at first: what does she do with them?

It was on a fine morning in June, and at the hour when children are seen on their way to the Sunday-school, that I saw the little girl come down the street. A sweet smile was on her face. I felt quite sure that she had a happy heart, and I could not but hope that she was one of Christ's dear lambs.

I passed over to the opposite side of the street, lest I should be noticed. She had gone only a few steps, when she met a little boy and his sister, who either knew little about Sunday as a holy day, or cared not to keep it. She stopped, and untied a piece of ribbon that was round her bundle; then drawing out two tracts, she gave them to the children, saying, 'I hope I shall not see you playing in the street next Sunday.'

On turning a corner at a short distance, I heard the voice of an aged woman: 'Here comes our little tract girl.' The child stopped again, and the old lady soon came to the door on crutches, for she was lame. 'I am glad to see you again, my darling,' said she; 'I have lived on that sweet tract you gave me last sabbath all through the week.' The little girl, with a smile and a few modest words, put two other tracts in her hand, and then bidding the aged woman 'good bye', passed on with nimble feet.

I stopped a moment to watch the old woman, as she stood at the door, looking at the titles of the tracts that had been given to her; then turning round, I saw a number of children at the corner of a street who were talking rather loudly. In the midst of them stood my little friend, picking from her bundle some small books, which were soon given to the children. I came up to them without being seen, and heard a little boy say to one who stood close beside him, and who I took to be a sister, 'Mary, do ask her to give us one more for father to read, and perhaps he will then let us go to the Sunday-school.' It seemed as if the little tract girl knew pretty well what they were wishing for, as she gave two of the little books to Mary, who cried, 'Oh, thank you,' as she quickly ran down the street.

I could keep silent no longer, but, going to her, asked what was her name. At first she was shy, for I was a stranger; but a few kind words won her confidence, and she began to talk with me. I said that I had seen her at her work of love, and hoped God would bless her in it. I then learned that her name was Anna, and that she went out on a Sunday morning to give away tracts.

I often thought of this happy meeting with the little tract girl, and intended to visit her, but had soon to leave the city, and did not return for many weeks. When I did return, it was to find that dear Anna was gone. She had been taken ill, and had soon died. But a few days before her death she had been on her last round with her tracts.

I saw her mother, who told me of the good her child had done, and of her faith and hope in Christ Jesus, to whom she looked as her Saviour; she spoke, too, of the sorrow that was shown by those Anna used to visit. I also learned that, through her labours, many children had been led to attend the sabbath-school, and it was hoped that more than one had been brought to seek the salvation of their souls.

May's Present.

This poor black woman is so grateful for the food given to her, that she is saying 'Thank you!' on her knees.

This poor black sailor and this little cabin-boy are ship-wrecked, and afloat on a raft. Their ship is quite deserted.

SOLD INTO SLAVERY

'KARL MARSH is sold into slavery!' said a man to me the other day.

'Sold into slavery!' I cried: 'is there anything like that now-a-days?'

'Indeed there is,' was the answer.

'Who bought him, pray?'

'Oh, it's a firm, and they own a good many slaves, and make shocking bad masters.'

'Can it be in these days? Who are they?' I asked.

'Well, they have agents everywhere, who tell a pretty good story, and so get hold of folk; but the names of the firm are Whisky and Wine.'

I had heard of them. It is a firm of bad reputation, and yet how extensive are their dealings! What town has not felt their influence? Once in their clutches, it is about the hardest thing in the world to break away from them. You are sold, and that is the end of it; sold to ruin sooner or later. I have seen people try to escape from them. Some, it is true, do make their escape; but the greater part are caught and go back to their chains.

He managed to drag the boy to the Convent Door.

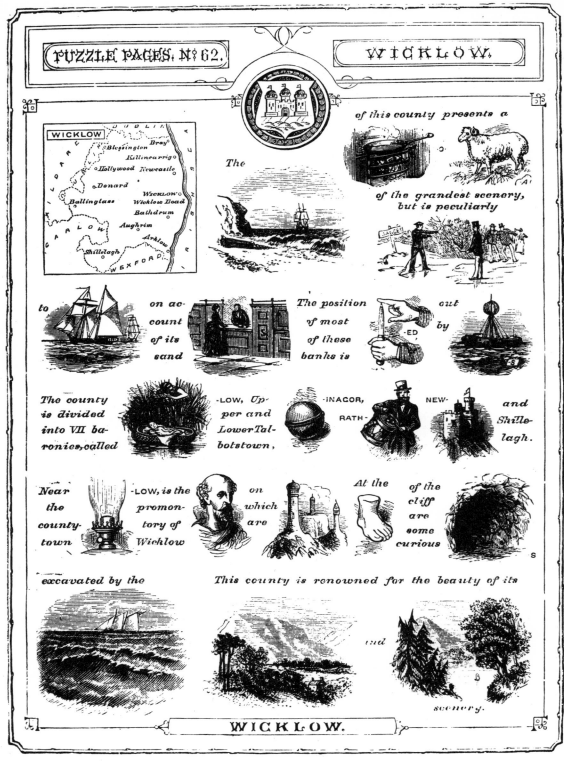

The [scenery] of this county presents a [scene] of the grandest scenery, but is peculiarly [dangerous] to [shipping] on account of its sand [banks]. The position of most of these banks is [mark]-ED out by [buoys].

The county is divided into VII baronies, called [New]-LOW, Upper and Lower Talbotstown, [New]-INACOR, RATH-[drum], NEW-[rath] and Shillelagh.

Near the county-town [Wick]-LOW, is the promontory of Wicklow [Head] on which are [ruins]. At the [foot] of the cliff are some curious [cave]S excavated by the [sea].

This county is renowned for the beauty of its [mountain] and [wood] scenery.

WICKLOW.

150

A Apple Pie

B bit it

C cut it

D dealt it

151

E   eat

it

F   fought

for it

G

got

it

H

had

it

J

joined

it

K

kept

it

L

longed

for

it

M

mourned

for

it

N

nodded

at it

O

opened

it

P

peeped

in it

Q

quartered

it

R

ran for it

S

stole it

T

took it

V

viewed it

W wanted it

all wished for
a piece in hand

THE MOUSE AND THE CAKE

A mouse found a beautiful piece of plum-cake,
The richest and sweetest that mortal could
    make;
'Twas heavy with citron and fragrant with
    spice,
And covered with sugar all sparkling as ice.

'My stars!' cried the mouse, while his eyes
    beamed with glee,
'Here's a treasure I've found; what a feast it will
    be;
But, hark! there's a noise, 'tis my brothers at
    play;
So I'll hide with the cake, lest they wander this
    way.

'Not a bit shall they have, for I know I can eat
Every morsel myself, and I'll have such a treat;'
So off went the mouse, as he held the cake fast;
While his hungry, young brothers went
    scampering past.

He nibbled, and nibbled, and panted, but still
He kept gulping it down till he made himself
    ill;
Yet he swallowed it all, and 'tis easy to guess,
He was soon so unwell that he groaned with
    distress.

His family heard him, and as he grew worse,
They sent for the doctor, who made him
    rehearse
How he'd eaten the cake to the very last crumb;
Without giving his playmates and relatives
    some.

'Ah me!' cried the doctor, 'advice is too late,
You must die before long, so prepare for your
    fate;
If you had but divided the cake with your
    brothers,
'Twould have done you no harm, and been
    good for the others.

'Had you shared it, the treat had been
    wholseome enough;
But eaten by *one*, it was dangerous stuff;
So prepare for the worst;' and the word had
    scarce fled,
When the doctor turned round, and the patient
    was dead.

Now all little people the lesson may take,
And *some* large ones may learn from the mouse
    and the cake;
Not to be over-selfish with what we may gain;
Or the best of our pleasures may turn into pain.

156

These boys are having a nice game in the play-ground belonging to the school. John has got a ball, and is trying to toss it into one of the caps.

School is over for the day, and now there is time to have a good long game at bowls before the tea-bell rings.

FURZE AND HEATHER FOR RAINY WEATHER

SEASIDE DANGERS

One day three children were playing on the sands, when the tide crept up and cut them off. But Tom bravely carried Agnes across first, and then came back for little Charlie.

NEVER PLAY WITH FIRE-ARMS

Charles, who was very fond of playing at sol-diers, one day carelessly took up his father's gun when it happened to be loaded, and nearly killed a dear little sister.

THE DANGEROUS CLIFF

These young folks had been warned of the dangerous cliff. They forgot this coming home, and little Edward fell over into the pool below. But he was fortunately rescued.

THROWING STONES

John, who was given to the bad habit of throwing stones, happened to throw one which struck a young lady, and was marched off to prison, where he remained all night.

PLAYING WITH GUNPOWDER

These foolish boys were bending over a train of gunpowder which they were about to fire, when a gentleman stamped out the light, thus saving them from a fearful accident.

FORBIDDEN FRUIT

These little folks have been eating some poisonous berries, which they had been told not to touch. They got better, but it was a narrow escape.

'Don't flog him, sir; he didn't break the window.'

'Say you're sorry!'

DO NOT BE VAIN

Florinda was very vain. When she went to a
party she was always thinking of her beauty
and her fine clothes; but this, as you may think,
quite spoilt her pleasure.

DO AS YOU ARE BID

Poor Mrs Clegg, who had to go out to work, told
Jane not to touch the fire. But Jane must needs
try to cook the dinner, and scalded her little
brothers and sisters.

THE LISTENER

'Listeners never hear any good of themselves.'
Here, for instance, is Michael, who hears that he
is disliked by everybody on account of this pry-
ing habit.

THE RAILWAY CARRIAGE

David had been told not to lean against the carriage door. Presently it flew open, and he was
thrown out. Luckily, however, he was not much
hurt, but he never forgot it.

165

'ONLY A PIN'

Amy had often been scolded for putting pins in her mouth. One day, when she was hastily dressing, she nearly swallowed one, and suffered greatly through this bad practice.

EDGED TOOLS

Master Matthew was always called Meddling Matt because he could never let anything alone. At last he cut himself very badly with a plane, —which made him more careful.

BEWARE OF THE GAS

By playing with the gas, Master Andrew caused a fearful explosion. The housemaid was much hurt, but, fortunately for Andrew's peace of mind, she recovered.

HEEDLESS SIDNEY

Heedless Sidney was always causing mischief and getting into trouble. One day he was trying to walk on a wall, when his foot slipped, and he tumbled into a pigsty!

A BAD JOKE

'Teasing Tom' was fond of practical jokes, and once frightened a poor maid-servant into a fit by coming upon her suddenly in a hideous mask.

LOST IN THE WOOD

Harriet and Edwin went to the wood without letting anyone know. A storm came on, and they lost their way; and it was a long time before their friends found them.

KATIE BRIGHTSIDE, AND HOW SHE MADE THE BEST OF EVERYTHING

NOT WEARY IN WELL-DOING

Katie's bright happy face looks brighter still to-day. Mabel has been kinder, done more to help in the house, and seems happier herself. It is above a year since they came to South Holme, and the summer has been hot. The yellow corn is waving in the fields, and in a few places it has been cut and is standing in graceful bending sheaves.

There is an errand to be done, and mamma would like Mabel to say, 'Let me go, mamma!' It is true she has been more busy than usual; but Mrs Reade knows that Katie's feet have hardly rested all the day, and that she must be tired. It is very hot, and scarcely any cool air comes through the open window, as Mabel throws herself down on the easiest chair. When we have been thinking of our own comfort, and for a long time caring most for self, it is not easy to learn new lessons, and to be unselfish all at once. Mabel thinks she has done a great deal to-

day, and I fear she is more proud than thankful as she looks back upon it.

'I want this little parcel taken to Mrs Ellis, who lives in that thatched cottage in Moor Lane. She is very poor, and has scarcely any clothes for her baby a few weeks old. I have made these from some old ones that Harry used to wear.'

'Why, that is nearly a mile away,' said Mabel. 'It is so hot, I am sure I cannot go so far. Beside, I don't like those low places. If the woman is ill, the cottage is sure to be dirty. Let Mary Ann go.'

'No, mamma, let me,' said Katie, starting up from her seat; 'Mary Ann's work is not done yet, and it is so nice to see a poor mother look glad when you send something for her child.'

Katie did not wait, but ran upstairs and put on her things.

The parcel was not heavy, and Mrs Reade gave Katie a sunshade, and told her to go slowly,

168

and not hurry back so as to overheat herself. So off she went, waving good-bye kisses to her little brothers, who were playing in the field.

Before she reached the cottage she met poor Dick, a half-witted lad, whom many of the children used to tease. They would run after him when there were several of them together, and would call him names until he was nearly wild with rage. But when alone, no child dared to tease poor Dick, for he was strong and could run fast, and in his anger might have done harm.

When Katie was half way she saw Dick coming towards her, and no one else was near. But she had no need to fear. More than once she had spoken to the village lads, and told them how cruel it was to tease him, who, by no fault of his own, was not so clever as they. And the brave child had even gone to Dick—much against Mabel's will—and taken his brown hand in hers, and led him gently from the teasing crowd to his own mother's door.

His mother loved him, the poor helpless lad, perhaps the more because he was so helpless, and was mocked and made game of by so many.

And she said with tears, 'God bless you, little miss, for being so good to my poor Dick! Perhaps some day even he may be of use to you. If not, God will not forget your act of love to one whom He has seen fit to afflict.'

As Dick met Katie he held out his hand, for the child often took him a little biscuit or sweet cake. She knew so small a thing would give him pleasure, and that small gift she always had at hand, in case she might meet the poor lad on the way.

So Katie never lost a chance of making somebody glad, and now she put out both her hands, that he might touch one, and find in which the sweets were hid. He gave a shout of joy, for he was right, and then, kind Katie laughing, opened her other hand and gave him more from that, so that poor Dick had double pleasure. Then on again she went to do her loving errand, forgetting that she was both hot and tired.

'Mamma said I was not to hurry,' thought Katie; 'so when I have told my message and given the parcel, I will stay and rest for awhile before I go back.'

'FLY-PAPERS! CATCH 'EM ALIVE!'

FLY-PAPERS, fly-papers! only a penny!
　They'll rid you of flies, be they few, be they
　　many.
In weather like this, who can bear to see flies
Tormenting the babe in his cradle who lies?

They tickle poor Grannie while reading her
　book,
And oh, how they worry and trouble the cook!
She can't bake a tart, or a hot joint prepare,
But those little marauders must have their full
　share.

Ask Dobbin, who lazily lies on the grass,
And for once in his life he'll agree with the ass:
They both feel a perfect disgust at the flies,
Who tickle their noses, their ears, and their
　eyes!

Just look at my hat! I caught every fly on it;
My wife caught as many: they're stuck on her
　bonnet.
Then come with your penny, a fly-paper buy,
I'll warrant you'll soon look in vain for a fly!

BE SURE YOUR SIN WILL FIND YOU OUT.

NUM. XXXII. 23.

'Father, I have sinned.'

172

THE NEW MOTHER

THE CHILDREN were always called Blue-Eyes and the Turkey. The elder one was like her dear father who was far away at sea; for the father had the bluest of blue eyes, and so gradually his little girl came to be called after them. The younger one had once, while she was still almost a baby, cried bitterly because a turkey that lived near the cottage suddenly vanished in the middle of the winter; and to console her she had been called by its name.

Now the mother and Blue-Eyes and the Turkey and the baby all lived in a lonely cottage on the edge of the forest. It was a long way to the village, nearly a mile and a half, and the mother had to work hard and had not time to go often herself to see if there was a letter at the post-office from the dear father, and so very often in the afternoon she used to send the two children. They were very proud of being able to go alone. When they came back tired with the long walk, there would be the mother waiting and watching for them, and the tea would be ready, and the baby crowing with delight; and if by any chance there was a letter from the sea, then they were happy indeed. The cottage room was so cosy: the walls were as white as snow inside as well as out. The baby's high chair stood in one corner, and in another there was a cupboard, in which the mother kept all manner of surprises.

'Dear children,' the mother said one afternoon late in the autumn, 'it is very chilly for you to go to the village, but you must walk quickly, and who knows but what you may bring back a letter saying that dear father is already on his way to England. Don't be long,' the mother said, as she always did before they started. 'Go the nearest way and don't look at any strangers you meet, and be sure you do not talk with them.'

'No, mother,' they answered; and then she kissed them and called them dear good children, and they joyfully started on their way.

The village was gayer than usual, for there had been a fair the day before. 'Oh, I *do* wish we had been here yesterday,' Blue-Eyes said as they went on to the grocer's, which was also the post-office. The post-mistress was very busy and just said 'No letter for you to-day.' Then Blue-Eyes and the Turkey turned away to go home. They had left the village and walked some way, and then they noticed, resting against a pile of stones by the wayside, a strange wild-looking girl, who seemed very unhappy. So they thought they would ask her if they could do anything to help her, for they were kind children and sorry indeed for any one in distress.

The girl seemed to be about fifteen years old. She was dressed in very ragged clothes. Round her shoulders there was an old brown shawl. She wore no bonnet. Her hair was coal-black and hung down uncombed and unfastened. She had something hidden under her shawl; on seeing them coming towards her, she carefully put it under her and sat upon it. She sat watching the children approach, and did not move or stir till they were within a yard of her; then she wiped her eyes just as if she had been crying bitterly, and looked up.

The children stood still in front of her for a moment, staring at her. 'Are you crying?' they asked shyly.

To their surprise she said in a most cheerful voice, 'Oh dear, no! quite the contrary. Are you?'

'Perhaps you have lost yourself?' they said gently.

But the girl answered promptly, 'Certainly not. Why, you have just found me. Besides,' she added, 'I live in the village.'

The children were surprised at this, for they had never seen her before, and yet they thought they knew all the village folk by sight.

Then the Turkey, who had an inquiring mind, put a question. 'What are you sitting on?' she asked.

'On a peardrum,' the girl answered.

'What is a peardrum?' they asked.

'I am surprised at your not knowing,' the girl answered. 'Most people in good society have one.' And then she pulled it out and showed it to them. It was a curious instrument, a good deal like a guitar in shape; it had three strings, but only two pegs by which to tune them. But the strange thing about the peardrum was not the music it made, but a little square box attached to one side.

'Where did you get it?' the children asked.

'I bought it,' the girl answered.

'Didn't it cost a great deal of money?' they asked.

'Yes,' answered the girl slowly, nodding her head, 'it cost a great deal of money. I am very rich,' she added.

'You don't look rich,' they said, in as polite a voice as possible.

'Perhaps not,' the girl answered cheerfully.

At this, the children gathered courage, and ventured to remark, 'You look rather shabby.'

'Indeed?' said the girl in a voice of one who had heard a pleasant but surprising statement. 'A little shabbiness is very respectable,' she added in a satisfied voice. 'I must really tell them this,' she continued. And the children wondered what she meant. She opened the little box by the side of the peardrum, and said, just as if she were speaking to some one who could hear her. 'They say I look rather shabby; it is quite lucky isn't it?'

'Why, you are not speaking to any one!' they said, more surprised than ever.

'Oh dear, yes! I am speaking to them both.'

'Both?' they said, wondering.

'Yes. I have here a little man dressed as a peasant, and a little woman to match. I put them on the lid of the box, and when I play they dance most beautifully.'

'Oh! let us see; do let us see!' the children cried.

Then the village girl looked at them doubtfully. 'Let you see!' she said slowly. 'Well, I am not sure that I can. Tell me, are you good?'

'Yes, yes,' they answered eagerly, 'we are very good!'

'Then it's quite impossible,' she answered, and resolutely closed the lid of the box.

They stared at her in astonishment. 'But we are good,' they cried, thinking she must have misunderstood them. 'We are very good. Then can't you let us see the little man and woman?'

'Oh dear, no!' the girl answered. 'I only show them to naughty children. And the worse the children the better do the man and woman dance.'

She put the peardrum carefully under her ragged cloak, and prepared to go on her way. 'I really could not have believed that you were good,' she said reproachfully, as if they had accused themselves of some great crime. 'Well, good day.'

'Oh, but we will be naughty,' they said in despair.

'I am afraid you couldn't,' she answered, shaking her head. 'It requires a great deal of skill to be naughty well.'

And swiftly she walked away, while the children felt their eyes fill with tears, and their hearts ache with disappointment.

'If we had only been naughty,' they said, 'we should have seen them dance.'

'Suppose,' said the Turkey, 'we try to be naughty to-day; perhaps she would let us see them to-morrow.'

'But, oh!' said Blue-Eyes, 'I don't know how to be naughty; no one ever taught me.'

The Turkey thought for a few minutes in silence. 'I think I can be naughty if I try,' she said. 'I'll try to-night.'

'Oh, don't be naughty without me!' she cried. 'It would be so unkind of you. You know I want to see the little man and woman just as much as you do. You are very, very unkind.'

And so, quarrelling and crying, they reached their home.

Now, when their mother saw them, she was greatly astonished, and, fearing they were hurt, ran to meet them.

'Oh, my children, oh, my dear, dear children,' she said; 'what is the matter?'

But they did not dare tell their mother about the village girl and the little man and woman, so they answered, 'Nothing is the matter,' and cried all the more.

'Poor children!' the mother said to herself, 'They are tired, and perhaps they are hungry; after tea they will be better.' And she went back to the cottage, and made the fire blaze; and she put the kettle on to boil, and set the tea-things on the table. Then she went to the little cupboard and took out some bread and cut it on the table, and said in a loving voice, 'Dear little children, come and have your tea. And see, there is the baby waking from her sleep; she will crow at us while we eat.'

But the children made no answer to the dear mother; they only stood still by the window and said nothing.

'Come, children,' the mother said again. 'Come, Blue-Eyes, and come, my Turkey; here is nice sweet bread for tea.' Then suddenly she looked up and saw that the Turkey's eyes were full of tears.

'Turkey!' she exclaimed, 'my dear little Turkey! what is the matter? Come to mother, my sweet.' And putting the baby down, she held out her arms, and the Turkey ran swiftly into them.

'Oh, mother,' she sobbed, 'Oh, dear mother! I do so want to be naughty. I do so want to be

very, very naughty.'

And then Blue-Eyes left her chair also, and rubbing her face against her mother's shoulder, cried sadly. 'And so do I, mother. Oh, I'd give anything to be very, very naughty.'

'But, my dear children,' said the mother, in astonishment, 'Why do you want to be naughty?'

'Because we do; oh, what shall we do?' they cried together.

'I should be very angry if you were naughty. But you could not be, for you love me,' the mother answered.

'Why couldn't we?' they asked.

Then the mother thought a while before she answered; and she seemed to be speaking rather to herself than to them.

'Because if one loves well,' she said gently, 'one's love is stronger than all bad feelings in one, and conquers them.'

'We don't know what you mean,' they cried; 'and we do love you; but we want to be naughty.'

'Then I should know you did not love me,' the mother said.

'If we were very, very, very naughty, and wouldn't be good, what then?'

'Then,' said the mother sadly—and while she spoke her eyes filled with tears, and a sob almost choked her—'then,' she said, 'I should have to go away and leave you, and to send home a new mother, with glass eyes and wooden tail.'

II

'Good-day,' said the village girl, when she saw Blue-Eyes and the Turkey approach. She was again sitting by the heap of stones, and under her shawl the peardrum was hidden.

'Are the little man and woman there?' the children asked.

'Yes, thank you for inquiring after them,' the girl answered; 'they are both here and quite well. The little woman has heard a secret—she tells it while she dances.'

'Oh do let us see,' they entreated.

'Quite impossible, I assure you,' the girl answered promptly. 'You see, you are good.'

'Oh!' said Blue-Eyes, sadly; 'but mother says if we are naughty she will go away and send home a new mother, with glass eyes and a wooden tail.'

'Indeed,' said the girl, still speaking in the same unconcerned voice, 'that is what they all say.' They all threaten that kind of thing. Of course really there are no mothers with glass eyes and wooden tails; they would be much too expensive to make.' And the common sense of this remark the children saw at once.

'We think you might let us see the little man and woman dance.'

'The kind of thing you would think,' remarked the village girl.

'But will you if we are naughty?' they asked in despair.

'I fear you could not be naughty—that is, really—even if you tried,' she said scornfully.

'But if we are very naughty to-night, will you let us see them to-morrow?'

'Questions asked to-day are always best answered to-morrow,' the girl said, and turned round as if to walk on. 'Good day,' she said blithely; 'I must really go and play a little to myself.'

For a few minutes the children stook looking after her, then they broke down and cried. The Turkey was the first to wipe away her tears. 'Let us go home and be very naughty,' she said; then perhaps she will let us see them to-morrow.'

And that afternoon the dear mother was sorely distressed, for, instead of sitting at their tea as usual with smiling happy faces, they broke their mugs and threw their bread and butter on the floor, and when the mother told them to do one thing they carefully did another, and only stamped their feet with rage when she told them to go upstairs until they were good.

'Do you remember what I told you I should do if you were very very naughty?' she asked sadly.

'Yes, we know, but it isn't true,' they cried. 'There is no mother with a wooden tail and glass eyes, and if there were we should just stick pins into her and send her away; but there is none.'

Then the mother became really angry, and sent them off to bed, but instead of crying and being sorry at her anger, they laughed for joy, and sat up and sang merry songs at the top of their voices.

The next morning quite early, without asking leave from the mother, the children got up and ran off as fast as they could to look for the village girl. She was sitting as usual by the heap of stones with the peardrum under her shawl.

'Now please show us the little man and woman,' they cried, 'and let us hear the peardrum. We were very naughty last night.' But the girl kept the peardrum carefully hidden.

'So you say,' she answered. 'You were not

half naughty enough. As I remarked before, it requires a great deal of skill to be naughty well.

'But we broke our mugs, we threw our bread and butter on the floor, we did everything we could to be tiresome.'

'Mere trifles,' answered the village girl scornfully. 'Did you throw cold water on the fire, did you break the clock, did you pull all the tins down from the walls, and throw them on the floor?'

'No, exclaimed the children, aghast, 'we did not do that.'

'I thought not,' the girl answered. 'So many people mistake a little noise and foolishness for real naughtiness,' And before they could say another word she had vanished.

'We'll be much worse,' the children cried, in despair. 'We'll go and do all the things she says;' and then they went home and did all these things. And when the mother saw all that they had done she did not scold them as she had the day before, but she just broke down and cried, and said sadly—

'Unless you are good to-morrow, my poor Blue-Eyes and Turkey, I shall indeed have to go away and come back no more, and the new mother I told you of will come to you.'

They did not believe her; yet their hearts ached when they saw how unhappy she looked, and they thought within themselves that when they once had seen the little man and woman dance, they would be good to the dear mother for ever afterwards.

The next morning, before the birds were stirring, the children crept out of the cottage and ran across the fields. They found the village girl sitting by the heap of stones, just as if it were her natural home.

'We have been very naughty,' they cried. 'We have done all the things you told us; now will you show us the little man and woman?' The girl looked at them curiously. 'You really seem quite excited,' she said in her usual voice. 'You should be calm.'

'We have done all the things you told us,' the children cried again, 'and we do so long to hear the secret'. We have been so very naughty, and mother says she will go away to-day and send home a new mother if we are not good.'

'Indeed,' said the girl. 'Well, let me see. When did your mother say she would go?'

'But if she goes, what shall we do?' they cried in despair. 'We don't want her to go; we love her very much.'

'You had better go back and be good, you are really not clever enough to be anything else; and the little woman's secret is very important; she never tells it for make-believe naughtiness.'

'But we did all the things you told us,' the children cried.

'You didn't throw the looking-glass out of the window, or stand the baby on its head.'

'No, we didn't do that,' the children gasped.

'I thought not,' the girl said triumphantly. 'Well, good-day. I shall not be here to-morrow.'

'Oh, but don't go away,' they cried. 'Do let us see them just once.'

'Well, I shall go past your cottage at eleven o'clock this morning,' the girl said. 'Perhaps I shall play the peardrum as I go by.'

'And will you show us the man and woman?' they asked.

'Quite impossible, unless you have really deserved it; make-believe naughtiness is only spoilt goodness. Now if you break the looking-glass and do the things that are desired...'

'Oh, we will,' they cried. 'We will be very naughty till we hear you coming.'

Then again the children went home, and were naughty, oh, so very very naughty that the dear mother's heart ached and her eyes filled with tears, and at last she went upstairs and slowly put on her best gown and her new sun-bonnet, and she dressed the baby all in its Sunday clothes, and then she came down and stood before Blue-Eyes and the Turkey, and just as she did so the Turkey threw the looking-glass out of the window, and it fell with a loud crash upon the ground.

'Good-bye, my children,' the mother said sadly, kissing them. 'The new mother will be home presently. Oh, my poor children!' and then weeping bitterly, the mother took the baby in her arms and turned to leave the house.

'But mother, we will be good at half-past eleven, come back at half-past eleven,' they cried, 'and we'll both be good; we must be naughty till eleven o'clock.' But the mother only picked up the little bundle in which she had tied up her cotton apron, and went slowly out at the door. Just by the corner of the fields she stopped and turned, and waved her handkerchief, all wet with tears, to the children at the window; she made the baby kiss its hand; and in a moment mother and baby had vanished from their sight.

Then the children felt their hearts ache with sorrow, and they cried bitterly, and yet they could not believe that she had gone. And the broken clock struck eleven, and suddenly there was a sound, a quick, clanging, jangling sound, with a strange discordant note at intervals. They rushed to the open window, and there they saw the village girl dancing along and playing as she did so.

'We have done all you told us,' the children called. 'Come and see; and now show us the little man and woman.'

The girl did not cease her playing or her dancing, but she called out in a voice that was half speaking half singing. 'You did it all badly. You threw the water on the wrong side of the fire, the tin things were not quite in the middle of the room, the clock was not broken enough, you did not stand the baby on its head.'

She was already passing the cottage. She did not stop singing, and all she said sounded like part of a terrible song. 'I am going to my own land,' the girl sang, 'to the land where I was born.'

'But our mother is gone,' the children cried; 'our dear mother will she ever come back?'

'No,' sang the girl, 'she'll never come back. She took a boat upon the river; she is sailing to the sea; she will meet your father once again, and they will go sailing on.'

Then the girl, her voice getting fainter and fainter in the distance, called out once more to them. 'Your new mother is coming. She is already on her way; but she only walks slowly, for her tail is rather long, and her spectacles are left behind; but she is coming, she is coming—coming—coming.'

The last word died away; it was the last one they ever heard the village girl utter. On she went, dancing on.

Then the children turned, and looked at each other and at the little cottage home, that only a week before had been so bright and happy, so cosy and spotless. The fire was out, the clock all broken and spoilt. And there was the baby's high chair, with no baby to sit in it; there was the cupboard on the wall, and never a sweet loaf on its shelf; and there were the broken mugs, and the bits of bread tossed about, and the greasy boards which the mother had knelt down to scrub until they were as white as snow. In the midst of all stood the children, looking at the wreck they had made, their eyes blinded with tears, and their poor little hands clasped in misery.

'I don't know what we shall do if the new mother comes,' cried Blue-Eyes. 'I shall never, never like any other mother.'

The Turkey stopped crying for a minute, to think what should be done. 'We will bolt the door and shut the window; and we won't take any notice when she knocks.'

All through the afternoon they sat watching and listening for fear of the new mother; but they saw and heard nothing of her, and gradually they became less and less afraid lest she should come. They fetched a pail of water and washed the floor; they found some rag, and rubbed the tins; they picked up the broken mugs and made the room as neat as they could. There was no sweet loaf to put on the table, but perhaps the mother would bring something from the village, they thought. At last all was ready, and Blue-Eyes and the Turkey washed their faces and their hands, and then sat and waited, for of course they did not believe what the village girl had said about their mother sailing away.

Suddenly, while they were sitting by the fire, they heard a sound as of something heavy being dragged along the ground outside, and then there was a loud and terrible knocking at the door. The children felt their hearts stand still. They knew it could not be their own mother, for she would have turned the handle and tried to come in without any knocking at all.

Again there came a loud and terrible knocking.

'She'll break the door down if she knocks so hard,' cried Blue-Eyes.

'Go and put your back to it,' whispered the Turkey, 'and I'll peep out of the window and try to see if it is really the new mother.'

So in fear and trembling Blue-Eyes put her back against the door, and the Turkey went to the window. She could just see a black satin poke bonnet with a frill round the edge, and a long bony arm carrying a black leather bag. From beneath the bonnet there flashed a strange bright light, and Turkey's heart sank and her cheeks turned pale, for she knew it was the flashing of two glass eyes. She crept up to Blue-Eyes. 'It is—it is—it is!' she whispered, her voice shaking with fear, 'it is the new mother!'

Together they stood with the two little backs against the door. There was a long pause. They thought perhaps the new mother had made up her mind that there was no one at home to let her in, and would go away, but presently the two children heard through the thin wooden door the new mother move a little, and then say to herself—'I must break the door open with my tail.'

For one terrible moment all was still, but in it the children could almost hear her lift up her tail, and then, with a fearful blow, the little painted door was cracked and splintered. With a shriek the children darted from the spot and fled through the cottage, and out at the back door into the forest beyond. All night long they stayed in the darkness and the cold, and all the next day and the next, and all through the cold, dreary days and the long dark nights that followed.

They are there still, my children. All through the long weeks and months have they been there, with only green rushes for their pillows and only the brown dead leaves to cover them, feeding on the wild strawberries in the summer, or on the nuts when they hang green; on the blackberries when they are no longer sour in the autumn, and in the winter on the little red berries that ripen in the snow. They wander about among the tall dark firs or beneath the great trees beyond. Sometimes they stay to rest beside the little pool near the copse, and they long and long, with a longing that is greater than words can say, to see their own dear mother again, just once again, to tell her that they'll be good for evermore—just once again.

And still the new mother stays in the little cottage, but the windows are closed and the doors are shut, and no one knows what the inside looks like. Now and then, when the darkness has fallen and the night is still, hand in hand Blue-Eyes and the Turkey creep up near the home in which they once were so happy, and with beating hearts they watch and listen; sometimes a blinding flash comes through the window, and they know it is the light from the new mother's glass eyes, or they hear a strange muffled noise, and they know it is the sound of her wooden tail as she drags it along the floor.

SPEAK THE TRUTH

SPEAK the truth for that is right,
  Whatsoe'er befall;
Let your hearts be clear as light,
  Open unto all.

Well you know deceit is sin,
  Satan loves a lie;
When a falsehood you begin
  He is waiting by.

PLEASE MIND THE SLIDE, SIR

I LIKE to see boys sliding on a cold winter day, if they do not trip one another up, as it warms them and does them good. But I do not like to see sliding on the pavement, as it makes walking dangerous, and many a person has fallen on a slide and injured himself very much. Some thoughtless boys, you see, have been making a slide on a path leading to the church. This is very wrong; and Ned Franks, one of the Sunday scholars, is warning the clergyman to mind not to walk upon it, it is so slippery. 'Please mind the slide, sir,' he is saying, and I am sure the clergyman is much obliged to him, for as he is just now thinking of little else except his text, he would probably have not seen it, and might have hurt himself very sadly. When Ned goes into the church presently to worship with the people, I am sure he will think with pleasure on his having saved the clergyman, perhaps, from a bad fall, for a kind word or a kind action is always a pleasant thing to think about afterwards.

A NOBLE DEED OF SELF-SACRIFICE

IT is rarely indeed that we hear of any one sacrificing their own lives to save that of another; still there are such cases on record, when to save some beloved child, parent or friend, a brave man or woman has laid down his or her own life readily and willingly. Very few are the instances in which a man will sacrifice his life to save one unknown to him. Here, however, is a case.

182

When on Christmas Day, 1871, the steamer *America* took fire, and sank at the mouth of the river La Plata, an Italian named Viale was swimming securely in the water well protected by a lifebelt. Unmarried and travelling alone, he had neither wife nor child to save. The waves however, brought just before him a young husband, who was making the most terrible exertions to save his beloved wife, whom he had but lately married, from the death which seemed so near to them. She is unconscious, the salt water is hanging heavily to her clothes, and on her pale, death-like face, the flames of the burning steamer are reflected: unspeakable anguish and distress are imprinted on the countenance of the young husband. Shall he let go his fainting charge, and, putting forth the remnant of all his strength, try and save himself? No! rather would he sink down with his helpless but beloved burden beneath the waves of that silvery stream. But for a minute longer can his strength hold out, then a watery grave must be the common lot of the attached young couple.

Viale witnesses this scene and then—what in that moment must have passed in his noble heart?—he looses the life-belt from round his waist, and gives it to the stranger. For a while he still continues to swim on, then he sinks down, paying for his generosity with his life. The name of the couple who were thus so nobly saved is Marco del Pont. It is they who relate the story.

SUSAN'S LETTER

'OH, Master Harry, would you mind putting that in the post as you go by, please, sir?'

'All right,' said Harry, 'taking the letter out of Susan's hand, and stuffing it into his pocket.

'If that's anything particular,' called out Dick, 'don't you give it to Harry. His head's a regular sieve; he'll just meet a fellow round the first corner, and never think about the letter again. You'd better pop round to the post yourself, Susan.'

'I can't, Master Dick; and it is very particular so you'll please try and remember it, Master Harry.'

'Of course I will, you've no need to fidget about it, Susan: I'm going straight off past the post-office first thing.'

Susan went back to her work, and the boys started off in different directions, for it was holiday-time, and each had his own friends and amusements. That day passed quietly, and so did the next, but the day after Susan was seen going about the house with red eyes and a pale, sad face. She was evidently in great trouble. Her mistress questioned her, and heard that the girl's cousin, who was a soldier, had written to say that his regiment had been ordered abroad, and that on their way to the coast they would have to pass through the town where Susan lived. They would have to wait twenty minutes in the station, and if Susan cared to come and say goodbye to her cousin, he would let her know what time the train would be in, and would get leave to speak to her.

'And you see, ma'am,' said Susan, with a sob, 'we've always thought a deal of each other' Tom and me, and I'm afraid something's put him out, for he's not written, and it was to-day they were coming through.'

But when Mrs Leslie heard that Susan had entrusted her letter to Harry's careless hands she was able to give the girl little comfort. No doubt the letter had been forgotten, and on inquiry this proved to be the case. There it lay in the heedless boy's pocket.

'I'm awfully sorry, Susan,' he said; 'I really did forget all about it. But look here, you shall see Cousin Tom; you shall, indeed. I know which train it is that waits here, and you'll let her come down to the station—won't you, mother? and we'll manage it between us.'

Mother readily gave her consent, and Harry, not being troubled with bashfulness, did manage it very well. Susan knew which company Tom belonged to, and Harry found out the offi- cer in charge of it, told the story of the letter and his own carelessness, and obtained leave for the cousins to have a few parting words.

Poor Tom was killed in his first battle, so Susan never saw him again; and Harry has learned to be more careful, for, as he says, he would never have forgiven himself if his forget- fulness had deprived Susan of those few minutes upon which she now looks back as some of the most precious of her life.

GOD'S CARE

OH, praise, the Lord for He is
    good,
He gives us life, and health, and
    food,
He watches o'er us night and day,
    And never turns His eyes away.

Young as we are, yet may we raise,
    Our feeble voices in His praise;
Weak as we are, the Lord above
    Will not despise an infant's love.

AN AWFUL STORY

THERE was once an awful little girl who had an 'awful' to everything. She lived in an awful house in an awful street, in an awful village, which was an awful distance from every other awful place. She went to an awful school, where she had an awful teacher, who gave her awful lessons out of awful books. Every day she was so awful hungry that she ate an awful amount of food, so that she looked awful healthy. Her hat was awful small, and her feet were awful large. When she took an awful walk, she climb- ed awful hills, and when she got awful tired she sat down under an awful tree to rest herself. In the summer she found herself awful hot, and in winter awful cold. When it didn't rain there was an awful drought, and when the awful drought was over there was an awful rain. So that this awful girl will come to an awful state, and if she does not get rid of this vulgar way of saying 'awful' about everything, I am afraid she will, by-and-by, come to an awful end.

TOYS FOR POOR CHILDREN

THERE are thousands of poor children in our hospitals and workhouses who are sadly off for want of toys to amuse them, and if the children of our well-to-do families would sometimes send them some of their old toys it would gladden their hearts very much indeed. So Mama told us the other day, just before Christmas, and we at once set to work to see what there was in the nursery we could spare. At first we thought there was not much, but when we examined we found many that we could spare very well. So little Lucy gave a lamb, Maria a doll, Henry a cart and a drum, and Rosa and Kate a ball, and a box of tea-things. These and some other things made quite a large parcel. So the day before Christmas Day, Mama sent for a fly, and the par- cel was placed in it, with another one made up by Papa and Mama, and we drove off to the workhouse. How much better it is to give away old toys in this way than to keep them all our- selves, as some selfish children do!

184

Getting ready for Christmas.

Chorus—We'll all put some crumbs outside the window-sill .

THE OLD COBBLER
AND THE CLERGYMAN

THERE are few men in the village who seem to have fewer comforts than old Thomas Barnes, the cobbler. He lives alone in that little wooden cottage yonder, and earns but a poor pittance, when he has done all he can. Yet the old man is very happy and contented, and is loved and respected by every one in the place, he is so good and so kind. There is not a child but likes to look at his cheerful face, and the worst lad in the place would be ashamed to be rude to the good old man. Many of the well-to-do people in the village go about surly and discontented; but it is never so with Thomas Barnes, for though I have known him now for many years I never knew him to look cross or discontented. The clergyman often stops in the street to talk to him, and shakes him by the hand, and calls him his 'old friend,' for he feels that old Thomas is a good Christian man, who is trying hard to live as a Christian man should. I wish we had everywhere more men like old Thomas Barnes.

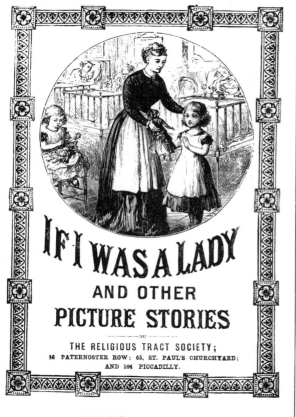

IF I WAS A LADY!

'IF I was a lady,' said a poorly dressed child, looking in at the goods displayed in a shop window, 'I'd have that dress with pink bows, and that bonnet with a yellow feather. Oh dear, how nice it must be to have plenty of money, so that you can buy all the pretty things you see!'

'If *I* was a lady,' said her companion, a quiet thoughtful-looking child, 'I suppose I should like nice clothes to wear; but I think it would

be so pleasant to give money to those who are very poor and sad and troubled.'

Time passed, and those two children grew up, not to be *ladies*, for that they could not be, but Fanny was a smart maid, who spent all her money on herself, and Mary was a steady-looking plainly dressed seamstress, who always seemed to have a shilling to spare for any one poorer than herself. Which do you think pleased God best?

AFTER A PLACE

LYDIA WHITE has just left off attending the village school because she is old enough to help her parents by earning a trifle towards her own support. She has always borne a good character for truthfulness, honesty, and industry, so she is likely to get on in the world if she does her best.

An old gentleman who often visited the school-house had noticed Lydia's bright rosy face and the quick replies she was ready to make to the teacher's questions; and when it came to his ears that she wanted a place, he told his servants that they must train the girl under them and make her into a useful woman. Lydia felt rather timid when she stood before the old gentleman, listening to what he required her to do; but she was glad to be taken into his service and said, 'I will try to please you.'

EDMUND'S REWARD

THIS is the picture of a little scene which took place in the schoolroom where Edmund Walters had been a pupil for several years. The boys had not made a favourite of him, for he was quiet and thoughtful and did not excel in the games of the playground; but the master used to say he had never had a more steady, painstaking lad under his care. Perhaps now and then Edmund was ready to envy those who seemed to know their lessons and get to the top of the class without any effort. But his reward for patient, earnest study has come this morning, when Mr Egerton walked into the schoolroom with his own young son by his side. 'I want a lad in my office whom you can speak well of,' he said to the master, 'one whom I can trust to do his work without being watched.'

Edmund is glad to be chosen, for he has a widowed mother to work for.

Wanted a boy.

191

'You bite just down to my thumb.'

HOSPITAL PLEASURES

HAVE you ever been to see one of the hospitals where little children are taken to be made better after some accident or illness? If not, perhaps you think it must be a sad place to visit; but I am sure you would be surprised to see such smiling faces and to hear such chattering tongues and such merry laughter coming from the rooms which are filled with the tiny patients

The children of the poor are often more happy than those of the rich, much more brave too in bearing pain and suffering; this is perhaps why they are more smiles than tears in one of these hospitals for the little ones. Then there are pleasures as well as pain, and one of these is the opening of some box or parcel of toys sent by a kind person who thinks of the delight a new doll or a picture-book will be. Can you not be one of these? For even your old playthings would be very welcome gifts.

GETTING BETTER

JOSEPHINE has had a very long illness. I could never count up the hours of pain she has been suffering; while the medicine she was forced to take filled as many bottles as would make a long row across the table. It is very hard to be ill in bed when others can go about and enjoy themselves; but if God sends us sickness, we must try to bear it, and be very obedient and gentle to those who have the care of us. Josephine has been very patient, and now her heart is full of gratitude, because she is getting better.

A week ago, her parents brought her down to the sea-shore; and every morning she is brought to the beach in a bath chair, and her sisters make a couch on which she can lie and enjoy the breeze. Sometimes they talk, sometimes they read; and very often Josephine likes best to be quiet, and think of God's goodness in making her better.

ONE THING AT A TIME

JANE has left off her business of sweeping and dusting the room, and is looking at the books which were placed on the table. Very likely it may be some good book which will do her no harm. Perhaps it has pictures in it of pleasant places far off; but whatever it may be, it would seem better if Jane finished her work first, for if her mistress finds the room not ready, she will see that the maid has been idling. Perhaps Jane has never heard the rhyme—

'One thing at a time, and that done well,
Is a very good rule as many may tell.'

For one would suppose by the picture that she is one of those people who like better to do two things at once if they can. This is a bad plan for children as well as for grown persons, and we shall find the Bible maxim that which answers best—'Whatsoever thy hand findeth to do, do it with all thy might.'

REMEMBER!

DICK was off to school for the first time. His parents felt it hard to part with their eldest boy; but they did it for his good, and that he might learn those useful things which should afterwards make him able to do his duty in the world.

Upon the last day at home Dick had a long talk with his mother; and when she took him to the railway-station her last word before he stepped into the train was, 'Remember!'

Shall I tell you what Dick had been told before, which it is to be hoped he would bear in mind? There were four special things.

Remember that God sees you.

Remember to pray to God.

Remember to do to others as you would they should do to you.

Remember Christ, who was patient and forgiving, when you are tempted to be angry.

194

The match boys.

The prisoner.

MAKING THE BEST OF IT

YES; making the best of the hard frost by enjoying healthy merry exercise, instead of cowering over a fire and shivering at every draught of air, as some girls do, while they murmur, 'It is wretchedly cold, I can't go out to-day.'

Frost and snow are very trying to the sick and weakly; the poor too, who are thinly clad and scantily fed, must feel it keenly; but it is a shame when the young and healthy grumble at the weather. These two girls felt very loath to jump out of bed this morning, but they did it at the right moment; they have not complained and made every one in the house uncomfortable with the sight of their descontented faces; and now, with their mother's leave, they have buckled on their skates, and their cheeks are all in a glow with the healthy exercise as they glide over the ice.

SAVED!

'TAKE CARE, Agnes,' Sophia had said so many times that her younger sister laughed and called her fidgety, and went on gathering pretty waving grasses quite near the water's edge as carelessly as ever. 'I shan't lose my footing,' she said; yet by-and-by there was a splash, a shrill scream, and the giddy child had fallen from the bank into the rapid stream.

Happily a woodman was at hand; and throwing down the ladder on which he had been mounted, he held on to it as he tried to rescue the sinking girl, while Sophia watched with pale face and frightened eyes, praying in her heart very earnestly for her sister. Though Agnes was saved from drowning, the fright and the coldness of the stream served to bring on an illness, in which she made many good resolutions for the future, which it is to be hoped she kept when she got well.

CATHERINE'S PRAYER

CATHERINE is a little orphan girl who is so unhappy as to live with people who never think of
asking God to bless them. But her parents had
early taught her to pray; and when Catherine is
alone for the night she kneels down and repeats
the words she used to say at her mother's knee.

> 'Look down in pity and forgive
>   Whate'er I've said or done amiss;
> And help me every day I live
>   To serve Thee better than in this.
>
> Now, while I speak, be pleased to take
>   A helpless child beneath Thy care;
> And condescend, for Jesus' sake,
>   To listen to my evening prayer.'

Once the woman who takes care of the little
orphan opened the door and heard these verses.
Perhaps she may learn from Catherine to think
of God and ask pardon for her sins.

GOOD-BYE!

NEVER was an elder brother better loved than
George Marshall; and he well deserved the affection of his little brothers and sisters, for he was
so very kind and never teazed them, after the
fashion of some big boys.

When I have told you this, you will not wonder that I say it was a sorrowful day in the cottage when news came of a place being found for
George in a town which was too far off for him
to come home every evening, as he had hoped
to do, now the time had come to get to work for
himself. The pet of the family was little Grace
and she was still in bed because it was so early
in the morning when George had to set out from
the cottage. 'Good-bye,' she cried, jumping up
and holding out her arms; and the big boy
kissed her fondly with tears in his eyes. I am
sure he will be a good kind man because he has
been so good in his home.

NURSERY NONSENSE,
or,
RHYMES WITHOUT REASON

But 'Nay, nay, nay;' they heard her say,
    The old Witch of the weather.

So in their tiny boat
    They sat, those sailors three;
Till the wind should blow, they couldna go
    A-sailing on the sea.

THE FAT MEN THREE

Sixteen men climb'd up a tree,
    And thirteen men got down;
And those three men, that were never seen
    again,
    Were the fattest men in town.

For, when in the sky the Sun rose high,
    And the south wind warm it blew,
Those fat men three on the top of the tree
    Were melted down to glue.

THE THREE BEGGARS

Three poor Beggar-men came to town,
    And they begg'd all day from door to door;
But they didn't get a bite from morn to night,
    So they said they would beg no more, no
    more

OLD WEATHERWITCH

'Blow, Wind, blow;'
    Three sailors sang together;

201

SING-SONG.

A NURSERY RHYME BOOK.

By CHRISTINA G. ROSSETTI.

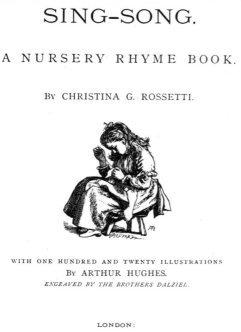

WITH ONE HUNDRED AND TWENTY ILLUSTRATIONS
By ARTHUR HUGHES.
ENGRAVED BY THE BROTHERS DALZIEL.

LONDON:
GEORGE ROUTLEDGE AND SONS,
THE BROADWAY, LUDGATE.
1872.

On the grassy banks
Lambkins at their pranks;
Woolly sisters, woolly brothers
Jumping off their feet
While their woolly mothers
Watch by them and bleat.

My baby has a father and a mother,
Rich little baby!
Fatherless, motherless, I know another
Forlorn as may be:
Poor little baby!

202

Mix a pancake,
Stir a pancake,
    Pop it in the pan;
Fry the pancake,
Toss the pancake,---
    Catch it if you can.

If a pig wore a wig,
    What could we say?
Treat him as a gentleman,
    And say 'Good day.'

If his tail chanced to fail,
    What could we do?---
Send him to the tailoress
    To get one new.

Sing me a song---
    What shall I sing?---
Three merry sisters
    Dancing in a ring,
Light and fleet upon their feet
    As birds upon the wing.

Tell me a tale---
    What shall I tell?---
Two mournful sisters,
    And a tolling knell,
Tolling ding and tolling dong,
    Ding dong bell.

Oh, fair to see
Bloom-laden cherry tree,
    Arrayed in sunny white;
    An April day's delight,
Oh, fair to see!

Oh, fair to see
Fruit-laden cherry tree,
    With balls of shining red
    Decking a leafy head,
Oh, fair to see!

Bread and milk for breakfast,
  And woollen frocks to wear,
And a crumb for robin redbreast
  On the cold days of the year.

There is one that has a head without an eye,
  And there's one that has an eye without a
    head:
You may find the answer if you try;
  And when all is said,
Half the answer hangs upon a thread!

My baby has a mottled fist,
  My baby has a neck in creases;
My baby kisses and is kissed,
  For he's the very thing for kisses.

Love me,—I love you,
  Love me, my baby;
Sing it high, sing it low,
  Sing it as may be.

Mother's arms under you.
  Her eyes above you
Sing it high, sing it low,
  Love me,—I love you.

What does the bee do?
  Bring home honey.
And what does Father do?
  Bring home money.
And what does Mother do?
  Lay out the money.
And what does baby do?
  Eat up the honey.

Baby cry—
  Oh fie!—
At the physic in the cup:
  Gulp it twice
  And gulp it thrice,
Baby gulp it up.

'I dreamt I caught a little owl.
  And the bird was blue—'
'But you may hunt for ever
And not find such an one.'

'I dreamt I set a sunflower,
  And red as blood it grew—'

'But such a sunflower never
Bloomed beneath the sun.'

Three plum buns
  To eat here at the stile
In the clover meadow,
  For we have walked a mile.

One for you, and one for me,
  And one left over:
Give it to the boy who shouts
  To scare sheep from the clover.

Dancing on the hill-tops,
  Singing in the valleys,
Laughing with the echoes,
  Merry little Alice.

Playing games with lambkins
  In the flowering valleys,
Gathering pretty posies,
  Helpful little Alice.

There's snow on the fields,
  And cold in the cottage,
While I sit in the chimney nook
  Supping hot pottage.

My clothes are soft and warm,
  Fold upon fold,
But I'm so sorry for the poor
  Out in the cold.

I have a Poll parrot,
  And Poll is my doll,
And my nurse is Polly,
  And my sister Poll.

Hopping frog, hop here and be seen,
  I'll not pelt you with stick or stone:
Your cap is laced and your coat is green;
  Good bye, we'll let each other alone.

Plodding toad, plod here and be looked at,
  You the finger of scorn is crooked at:
But though you're lumpish, you're harmless
    too;
  You won't hurt me, and I won't hurt you.

206

Where innocent bright-eyed daisies are,
  With blades of grass between,
Each daisy stands up like a star
  Out of a sky of green.

The days are clear,
  Day after day,
When April's here,
  That leads to May,
And June
Must follow soon:
  Stay, June, stay!—
If only we could stop the moon
And June!

A peach for brothers, one for each
  A peach for you and a peach for me;
But the biggest, rosiest, downiest peach
  For Grandmamma with her tea.

A baby's cradle with no baby in it,
  A baby's grave where autumn leaves drop
    sere;
The sweet soul gathered home to Paradise,
  The body waiting here.

207

The rose with such a bonny blush,
   What has the rose to blush about?
If it's the sun that makes her flush,
   What's in the sun to flush about?

Three little children
   On the wide wide earth
Motherless children—
   Cared for from their birth
     By tender angels.

Three little children
   On the wide wide sea,
Motherless children—
   Safe as safe can be
     With guardian angels.

208

ABROAD

WHILE chatting with Dennis, Rose lost all her fear ;
    And the swift Albert Victor came safe to the pier
At Boulogne, where they landed, and there was the train
In waiting to take up the travellers again.
But to travel so quickly was not their intent :
On a little refreshment our party was bent.
Here they are at the Buffet—for dinner they wait—
And the tall *garçon*, André, attends them in state.

At a separate table sits Monsieur Legros,
And behind him his poodle, Fidèle, you must know,
Who can dance, he's so clever, and stand on his head,
Or upon his nose balance a morsel of bread.
Mabel takes up some sugar to coax him, whilst Nell
Calls him to her—Fidèle understands very well—
"Why! he must have learnt English, he knows what we say,"
Mabel cries, "See!—he begs in the cleverest way."

THEN to the Hotel on the quay they all went;
    To remain till the morrow they all were content:
After so much fatigue Father thought it was best,
For the children were weary and needed the rest.
Pictured here is the room in that very Hotel,
Where so cosily rested Rose, Mabel, and Nell.

Mabel dreamed of the morrow—of buying French toys:
Rose remembered the steam-pipe, and dreamed of its noise.
Nellie's dreams were of home, but she woke from her trance
Full of joy, just to think they were *really* in France.
            Very early next morning, you see them all three
            Looking out from their window that faces the sea.

CHILDREN are happy with "Sister" all day,
Mothers can't nurse them—they work far away.
Good Sister Rosalie, she is so kind,
E'en when they're troublesome, she doesn't mind.
Here in the first room the Babies we see, sitting at *dejeuner* round Rosalie.

Dodo is crying, he can't find his spoon—some one will find it and comfort him soon.
Over yon cradle bends kind Sister Claire,
Dear little Mimi is waking up there.
Sister Félicité, sweetly sings she,
"Up again, down again, *Bèbé*, to me."

ARRIVAL AT CAEN.

THROUGH Rouen when our friends had been,
    And all its famous places seen,
They travelled on, old Caen to see,
Another town in Normandy.

Arrived at Caen, the travellers here
Before the chief Hotel appear,
Miss Earle, Rose, Bertie you descry—
The rest are coming by-and-by.

Monsieur le Maitre, with scrape and bow,
Stands ready to receive them now,
And Madame with her blandest air,
And their alert *Commissionaire*.

NEXT up the staircase see them go,
    With *femme de chambre* the way to show.
Father and Dennis; standing there,
Are asking for the bill of fare.

Monsieur le Maitre, who rubs his hands
And says, "What are *Monsieur's* commands?"
With scrape and bow, again you see—
The most polite of men is he.

"L'HOMME qui passe," in France they call
  The man who thrives
  By grinding knives—
Who never stays at home at all,

  But always must be moving on.
    He's glad to find
    Some knives to grind,
  But when they're finished he'll be gone.

  With dog behind to turn the wheel,
    He grinds the knife
    For farmer's wife,
  And pauses now the edge to feel :

    The dog behind him hears the sound
      Of cheerful chat
      On this and that,
    And fears no knife is being ground.

      The man makes jokes with careless smile,
        He doesn't mind
        The dog behind,
      But goes on talking all the while.

THE

KNIFE-GRINDER

OF CAEN.

CHOCOLATE AND MILK.

LITTLE Lili, whose age isn't three years quite,
  Went one day with Mamma for a long country walk,
Keeping up, all the time, such a chatter and talk
Of the trees, and the flowers, and the cows, brown and white.
Soon she asked for some cake, and some chocolate too,
For this was her favourite lunch every day—
" Dear child," said Mamma, "let me see—I dare say

" If I ask that nice milkmaid, and say it's for you,
Some sweet milk we can get from her pretty white cow."
" I would rather have chocolate," Lili averred.
Then Mamma said, " Dear Lili, please don't be absurd ;
My darling, you cannot have chocolate now :
You know we can't get it so far from the town.—
Come and stroke the white cow,—see, her coat 's soft as silk."
" But, Mamma," Lili said, "if the *White* cow gives milk,
Then chocolate surely must come from the *Brown*."

FOR Paris quite an early start
    They made the following day,
And out of windows every one
Kept looking, all the way.
And many a pretty road like this
The train went whizzing past,
Where gatekeeper, with flag and horn,
Stood by the gates shut fast.
That's Marie you see standing there :
Now, do you wonder why
A *woman* has to blow the horn
Before the train goes by ?—
Her husband is a lazy man,
He's in his cottage near,
He would not stir a step, although
The train will soon be here.
And Marie called him, " Paul, be quick—
Go shut the gate," she cried—
" Don't hurry me, there's time enough,"
The lazy man replied.
So Marie had to go, you see,
And take the horn, and blow.—
And every day it's just the same,
She always has to go.

JARDIN d'ACCLIMATATION
50 CENTIMES
PRÉSENTER CE BILLET À TOUTE RÉQUISITION
VALABLE pour le Jour même
3 MAI 82
A89865

MUMBO and Jumbo, two elephants great,
From India travelled, and lived in state,
In Paris the one, and in London the other :
Now Mumbo and Jumbo were sister and brother.
A warm invitation to Jumbo came,
To cross the Atlantic and spread his fame.
Said he, " I really don't want to go—
But then, they're so pressing!—I can't say No!"

So away to America Jumbo went,
But his sister Mumbo is quite content
To stay with the children of Paris, for she
Is as happy an elephant as could be :
" I've a capital house ; quite large and airy,
Close by live the Ostrich and Dromedary,
And we see our young friends every day," said she ;
" Oh, where is the Zoo' that would better suit me ?"

JARDIN D'ACCLIMATATION
TRAMWAYS
LE LAC DU JARDIN
à la
PORTE MAILLOT
35 CENTIMES
3 MA 82
D01837

PARIS, gay Paris! so bright and so fair,
  Your sun is all smiles, and there's mirth in your air.

The children, though tired with their travelling, found
That the first night in Paris one's sleep is not sound,
For the hum of the streets makes one dream all the night
Of the wonderful sights that will come with the light.

The morning was fine, and—breakfast despatched—
They soon made their way to the Gardens attached
To the old Royal Palace, and there met a throng
Of French children, and joined in their games before long.

One boy lent his hoop, and gave Bertie a bun,
And—talking quite fast—seemed to think it great fun
With nice English girls like our Nellie to play,
Though not understanding a word she might say.

On leaving the Gardens, the party were seated
Outside of a *café*, and there Papa treated
Them all to fine ices and chocolate too ;
They could hardly tell which was the nicer—could you?

Paris, gay Paris,
  So bright and so fair !
Your sun is all smiles.
  .And there's mirth in your air !

ROSE and Bertie have a ride;
  Mabel, walking at their side,
Carries both the dolls, and so
By the Luxembourg they go.

Over in that Palace soon—
For the clock is marking noon—
The "Senate" will together come
(Like our "House of Lords" at home).

IN THE
LUXEMBOURG GARDENS.

Hear that woman, "Who will buy
Windmill, ball, or butterfly"—
Josephine and Phillipe, see,
Eager as they both can be.

Charles before her, silent stands,
With no money in his hands,
No more *sous*—he spent them all
On that big inflated ball.

Be content, my little friend,
Money spent you cannot spend;
With your good St. Bernard play,
Buy more toys another day.

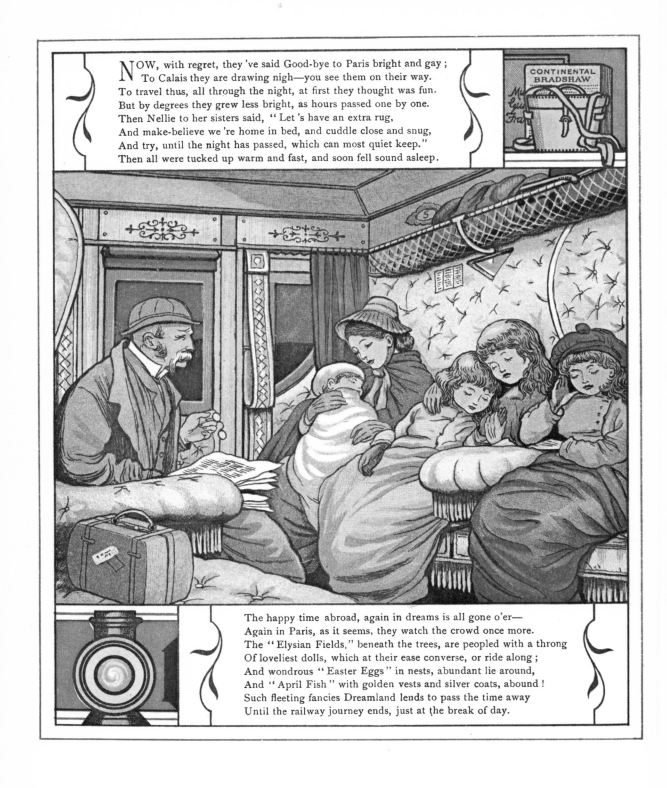

NOW, with regret, they 've said Good-bye to Paris bright and gay ;
    To Calais they are drawing nigh—you see them on their way.
To travel thus, all through the night, at first they thought was fun.
But by degrees they grew less bright, as hours passed one by one.
Then Nellie to her sisters said, " Let 's have an extra rug,
And make-believe we 're home in bed, and cuddle close and snug,
And try, until the night has passed, which can most quiet keep."
Then all were tucked up warm and fast, and soon fell sound asleep.

CONTINENTAL
BRADSHAW

The happy time abroad, again in dreams is all gone o'er—
Again in Paris, as it seems, they watch the crowd once more.
The " Elysian Fields," beneath the trees, are peopled with a throng
Of loveliest dolls, which at their ease converse, or ride along ;
And wondrous " Easter Eggs" in nests, abundant lie around,
And " April Fish " with golden vests and silver coats, abound !
Such fleeting fancies Dreamland lends to pass the time away
Until the railway journey ends, just at the break of day.

SONGS FOR LITTLE PEOPLE

by

NORMAN GALE

THE DEW

THE-RAINBOW-

Hardly any youngster knows
What the dew is on a rose.

If you children all are nice
I will teach you in a trice.

Long ago when men were sage,
(This was in the Golden Age,)

They were certain lovely-lipped,
Meadow-haunting fairies tripped

Night by night in starlit reels
Practising their fragile heels.

But to-day to hosts and hosts
Fairies are less real than ghosts.

So at night the fairies weep
While the unbelievers sleep;

And, while grieving out of view,
Change their sorrows into dew.

Whence, my children, it appears
There's no salt in fairies' tears!

THREE fairies climbed a rainbow hill;
And two were Jacks, and one a Jill.

Each clambered up a coloured lane,
In pleasure dreaming not of pain.

At last the heavenly beamy belt
Began in lessening love to melt;

Whereat the fairies through the arch
Fell headlong in a wood of larch.

Each, being hurt in leg and arm,
Was carried to a fairies' farm,

Where comrades gave them creamy milk,
And dressed their wounds in softest silk.

A doctor came, who smiled and said,
A rainbow was less safe than bed.

So this the moral you must scan—
Not where you wish, but where you can.

A MIDNIGHT DANCE

This boy will tell you, I am sure,
How moon and mouse played on the floor;
But he can tell a stranger thing
Of fairy fiddle and magic string.

Nurse says his eyes are far away,
He cannot play as others play;
And so, perhaps, the fairies came
To cheer him with a midnight game.

His room was full of friendly beams,
Ladders of fancy, light of dreams;
The moon had placed a shiny hand
On carpet, bed, and washing-stand.

The mouse within the silver lake
Was nibbling crumbs of currant cake,
When thirty fairies bright to see
Appeared in gauzy company.

The girls in sheeny petticoats,
Singing delicious treble notes,
With moving mazes charmed the eye,
Adepts in dance and minstrelsy.

And then came marching from the door,
With steady steps across the floor,
Fairies, made servants for theirs sins,
With tiny golden violins.

These formed a group beside the bed;
Each bent his small obedient head,
And then was scraped a dance so sweet
It captured all the hearers' feet.

Oh, how they flitted! how they leapt!
In magic undulations swept!
And how the fiddlers' fiery bows
Cried FASTER to the tripping toes!

Most rare and lovely was the view—
The twist of red, the flash of blue!
The mouse unfrightened, stared to see
The skipping hues of revelry.

Suddenly stopped the dancing din,
The fiddlers fled, the moon went in;
'Twas thus the kindly fairies came
To show this boy a midnight game.

226

THANKS

Thank you very much indeed,
River, for your waving reed;
Mr Sun, for jolly beam;
Mrs Cow, for milk and cream;
Hollyhocks, for budding knobs;
Foxgloves, for your velvet fobs;
Pansies, for your silly cheeks;
Chaffinches, for singing beaks;
Spring, for wood anemones
Near the mossy toes to trees;
Summer, for the fruited pear,
Yellowing crab and cherry fare;
Autumn, for the bearded load,

Hazel-nuts along the road;
Winter, for the fairy tale,
Spitting log and bouncing hail;
Christmas Day, for Mary's Child,
Jesus manifest and mild.

But, blest Father high above,
All these joys are from your love;
And your children everywhere,
Born in palace, lane, or square,
Cry, with voices all agreed,
THANK YOU VERY MUCH INDEED!

228

East & West

All the men of the West are here
With gauntlet, pipeclay, horse, and spear;
All the men of the East are come
With bugle, standard, fife, and drum.

Though each may bluster like a foe,
I do not think much blood will flow;
But every man of the West, at least,
Will stare very hard at the men from the East.

You all remember father's looks
When you have inked his pretty books;
Such stares will pierce each scarlet breast,
And stab the hearts of the men from the West.

If they are wise they will delight
In peace, for only sillies fight;
'Tis best that they should take the train
For home and mother's kiss again.

229

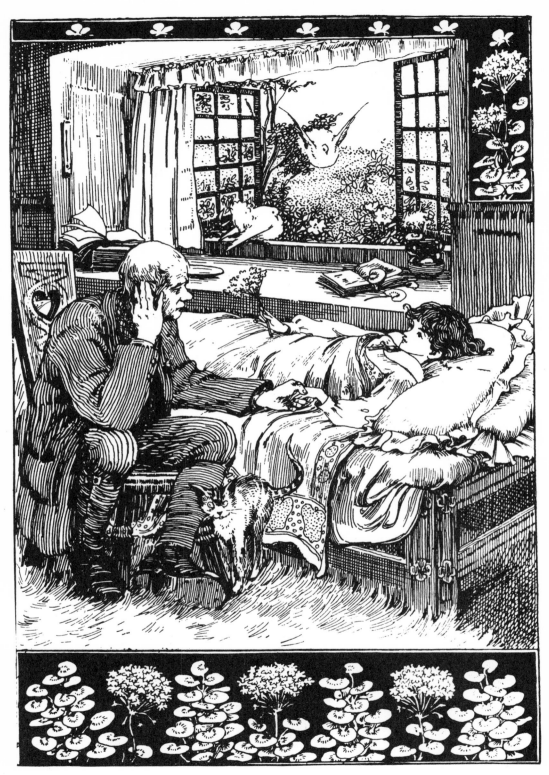

THE WINDOW-BOX

O Timothy Trot in the roses and cloves,
So cross if your peas are removed by my doves,
Remember the gift that your favourite loves—
  A window-box full of geraniums.

The doctor has been with his brow full of cares,
And he says that the death in my back is past
    prayers;
So bring me, dear Timothy, quickly upstairs
  A window-box full of geraniums.

I leave you the heir to my rabbits and mice,
Give Tommy my skates for his fun on the ice,
And all I shall charge is a blossomy price—
  A window-box full of geraniums.

Please tidy my garden for sweet Cousin Bess,
I've planted potatoes and pansies and cress;
She'll water and gather. I only possess
  A window-box full of geraniums.

O freckled and faithful! O Timothy Trot!
No more we shall manage the pinks in the plot;
But keep in full bloom, just to brighten my lot,
  A window-box full of geraniums.

I think you will cry to the roses and cloves,
I'm sure you will pardon the beaks of the
    doves,
I know you will bring what your favourite
    loves—
  A window-box full of geraniums.

231

THE MAKESHIFT

Tired, darling?
   Come and rest
That tangled mop
   On Auntie's breast!

She does not know
   I have, at best,
A make-believe
   For mother's breast.

Oh, never was
   So sweet a guest
To touch the heart
   In Auntie's breast.

My precious bird,
   Be this thy nest;
And fall asleep
   On Auntie's breast.

CRADLE SONG

BEES are resting sugary thighs,
Stars awake in the evening skies,
Timothy, Timothy, close your eyes,
   King of the cradle, sleep.

Sleep, my honey; O sleep, my star,
Dream where the rainbow ribbons are,
Ride with the Queen in the Fairies' car.
   King of the cradle, sleep.

Father is tossing upon the sea,
Timothy rocks at home with me;
Weary of trumpet, cannon, and knee,
   King of the cradle, sleep.

God, whose babes are many and far,
Keep him from craft, and save from war;
Give to my rose from a golden star,
   Honey and innocent sleep.

BARTHOLOMEW

Bartholomew
  Is very sweet,
From sandy hair
  To rosy feet.

Bartholomew
  Is six months old,
And dearer far
  Than pearls or gold.

Bartholomew
  Has deep blue eyes,
Round pieces dropped
  From out the skies.

Bartholomew
  Is hugged and kissed!
He loves a flower
  In either fist.

Bartholomew's
  My saucy son:
No mother has
  A sweeter one!

TUBBING

Uncle Harry, hear the glee
Coming from the nursery!
Shall we just pop in to see
  Thomas in his tub?

In a soapy pond of joy,
Water as his only toy,
Sits my golden sailor-boy
  Thomas in his tub.

There he is, the little sweet,
Clutching at his rosy feet!
Make your toes and kisses meet,
  Thomas in the tub!

Partly come of fairy line,
Partly human, part divine,
How I love this rogue of mine,
  Thomas in the tub!

ANGELA'S BIRTH

Angela came to us out of the flowers,
God's little blossom that changed into ours.

Cloves for her fingers, and cloves for her toes,
Eyes from the succory, mouth from the rose.

Loveliness sprang from the sisterly stocks,
Daffodils gave her those yellowy locks.

Fairies that visit her constantly meet
Lilies and lavender making her sweet.

Cherry-pie, pansy, forget-me-not, musk,
Wake in her dawning and sleep in her dusk.

Angela came to us out of the flowers,
God's little blossom that changed into ours.

AUNTIE NELL

We have to stay in bed
    Till Auntie comes up-stairs;
And then we cluster round her knees
    To say our prayers.

And after asking God
    To keep us good and sweet,
Dear Nursie does her very best
    To make us neat.

But if we go for a walk,
    Or ride the pony Bell,
It is not fun unless we have
    Our Auntie Nell.

We look in every room,
    But mother is not there;
She's never, never in the house,
    Or anywhere.

Yet, Daddy says, some day
    We'll find her bright and well;
Till then we must contrive to do
    With Auntie Nell.

BIBLIOGRAPHICAL NOTES

Illustrations by Samuel Williams.
first published 1842.

THE AFRICAN MONITOR GIRL.
London: Religious Tract Society.
n.d. pp. 8. 9.1 × 6.3 cm.   61–2

On Seeing the Bible Society's New
Collecting Box from ILLUSTRATED
SONGS AND HYMNS FOR THE
LITTLE ONES. Compiled by
Uncle John. London: Messrs Par-
tridge & Co. [*ca* 1858]. pp. [viii]
202. 25.1 × 16.7 cm.   62
by F. P. illustrated by H. Anelay.

MY FIRST LESSON BOOK TO TEACH
ME SPELLING AND READING.
illustrated by forty engravings.
London: Thomas H. Keble. [*ca*
1850]. pp. [16]. 20.5 × 16.3 cm.   63–6

THE DEATH AT SCHOOL. TRUE
SKETCHES FROM LIFE, 3. London:
Houlston & Stoneman. n.d. pp. 8.
10.3 × 6.6 cm. Farthing Series.
No. 76.   67

Tit Bits for Tiny Wits from BIR-
DIE'S BOOK. London: George
Routledge and Sons. 1880. pp.
[24]. 12 × 9 cm.   68–9

ABOUT UGLY IDOLS. Leicester:
Published by Winks and Son. n.d.
pp. 8. 10 × 6.7 cm. Grandfather's
Tales.   70

HARRY'S RASH WISH, AND HOW
THE FAIRIES GRANTED IT. London: Frederick Warne. [*ca* 1888].
pp. [64]. 16.3 × 10.5 cm.   73–8
by Mary Ellen Greene.
Illustrations by R. Huskisson.

Queen Victoria and the Bible from
MY PET'S ALBUM. with 130 illustrations by First-Class Artists.
London: S. W. Partridge & Co.
n.d. pp. 272. 21.3 × 16.7 cm.   78–9
illustration by Henry Anelay.

A Welcome Guest from Robin's Nest
from BIRDIE'S BOOK. London: 81–2,
George Routledge and Sons. 1880.   85–6, 89
pp. [24]. 12 × 9 cm.

THE COTTAGE CHILD. London: Religious Tract Society. n.d. pp. 8.

9.1 × 6.1 cm.   89–90

THE PEEP OF DAY, OR, A SERIES
OF THE EARLIEST RELIGIOUS
INSTRUCTION THE INFANT MIND
IS CAPABLE OF RECEIVING. with
Verses illustrative of the Subjects.
hundred and nineteenth thousand,
revised and corrected. London:
Thomas Hatchard. 1859. pp. xx.
264. 14.4 × 9 cm.   90, 93, 95–6
by Favel Lee Mortimer.
first published in 1833.

TEMPER; OR THE STORY OF SUSAN
AND BETSY. London: Religious
Tract Society; J. Davis; J. Nisbet.
n.d. pp. 16. 10 × 6.6 cm.   96–7

Little Kisses for Little Misses from
BIRDIE'S BOOK. London: George
Routledge and Sons. 1880. pp.   100, 102,
[24]. 12 × 9 cm.   104

HOME! SWEET HOME! Leicester:
Published by Winks and Son. n.d.
pp. 8. 10.4 × 6.6 cm. Grandfather's Tales.   104, 107

LITTLE MARY'S PICTURE RIDD-
LES. with two hundred illustrations. London: David Bogue.
[*ca* 1858]. pp. 32. 17.4 × 13.4 cm.
Little Mary's Book.   107–8

Little Mites for Tiny Sprites from
BIRDIE'S BOOK. London: George
Routledge and Sons. 1880. pp.
[24]. 12 × 9 cm.   111–2

MEMOIRS OF A LONDON DOLL.
Written by Herself. edited by Mrs
Fairstar [*pseudonym*]. London:
Henry G. Bohn. 1855. pp. 127.
17 × 12.8 cm.   115–6
by Richard Henry Horne.
illustrations by Margaret Gillies.

The Band of the Red, White and Blue
from THE INFANTS' MAGAZINE.
Vol. 24. London: S. W. Partridge
& Co. 1891. pp. [iv] 188. 20.9 ×
15.8 cm.   116

'*Drive to Bethnal Green*' from THE
LENT JEWELS, AND OTHER
TALES. London: George Routledge
and Sons. [*ca* 1884]. pp. 77–149.

illustrated by Archibald Chasemore.

Remember! from MAKING THE BEST OF IT, AND OTHER PICTURE STORIES. London: The Religious Tract Society. n.d. pp. 12. 17.1 × 11.7 cm. 194

Making the Best of it from MAKING THE BEST OF IT, AND OTHER PICTURE STORIES. London: The Religious Tract Society. n.d. pp. 12. 17.1 ×11.7 cm. 197

Saved! from IF I WAS A LADY, AND OTHER PICTURE STORIES. London: The Religious Tract Society. n.d. pp. 12. 17.1 ×11.7 cm. 197

Catherine's Prayer from MAKING THE BEST OF IT, AND OTHER PICTURE STORIES. London: The Religious Tract Society. n.d. pp. 12. 17.1 ×11.7 cm. 198

Good-Bye! from IF I WAS A LADY, AND OTHER PICTURE STORIES. London: The Religious Tract Society. n.d. pp. 12. 17.1 ×11.7 cm. 198

NURSERY NONSENSE; OR, RHYMES WITHOUT REASON. London: Griffith and Farran. 2nd edition. 1865. pp. viii.56. 18.5 ×13.5 cm. *by D'Arcy Wentworth Thompson. illustrated by Charles Henry Bennett.* 200–1

SING-SONG. A NURSERY RHYME BOOK. London: George Routledge and Sons. 1872. pp. xii. 130. 18.8 ×13.5 cm. *by Christina Georgina Rossetti. illustrated by Arthur Hughes.* 202–8

SONGS FOR LITTLE PEOPLE. Westminster: Archibald Constable & Company. 1896. pp. viii. 110. 21.7 ×13.5 cm. *by Norman Cale. Illustrated by Helen Stratton.* 225–35

The colour plates are taken from:
ABROAD. illustrated by Thomas Crane and Ellen E.Houghton. London: Marcus Ward & Co. [*ca* 1882].

GRANDMAMMA EASY'S MERRY MULTIPLICATION. London: Dean & Co. [*ca* 1840].

LITTLE CHARLES AND HIS DOG. London: J.L. Marks. [*ca* 1840]. Aunty Jaunty's Tales.

LITTLE ANN OTHER POEMS. by Jane and Ann Taylor. illustrated by Kate Greenaway. London and New York: George Routledge & Sons. [*ca* 1883].

MUSICAL VISITORS TO A QUIET STREET. London: Dean and Son. [*ca* 1860].

OUR OLD FRIENDS' BALL. London: Dean & Son. [*ca* 1860]. Mamma Lovechild's Series.

THROUGH THE MEADOWS. by Frederick Edward Weatherly. illustrated by Mary Ellen Edwards. London: Hildesheimer and Faulkner. [*ca* 1885].

THE TOWN AND COUNTRY TOY BOOK. London: The Religious Tract Society. [*ca* 1880].

UNDER THE MISTLETOE. by Robert Ellice Mack. illustrated by Lizzie Lawson. London: Griffith, Farran & Co. [*ca* 1886].

THE WONDERS OF A TOY-SHOP. London: Dean & Co.

The full-page black and white illustrations are taken from:
CHATTERBOX
THE CHILD'S COMPANION
THE CHILDREN'S FRIEND
THE CHILDREN'S TREASURY
FINE FEATHERS AND FLUFFY FUR by Aunt Ethel
THE INFANTS' MAGAZINE
LITTLE WIDE-AWAKE
MY PET'S ALBUM
"OUR DARLINGS"
THE PRIZE FOR GIRLS AND BOYS
SUNNY FACES. A PICTURE BOOK FOR HAPPY HOURS by D.J.D.

THOUGHTFUL JOE, AND HOW HE GAINED HIS NAME by Ruth Lamb
THE YOUNG COASTERS. STORIES AND VERSES FOR LITTLE PEOPLE